Honey Creek Work Weekend

O ne of the virtues and handicaps of a volunteer organization such as the Wisconsin Society for Ornithology is that it is wholly dependent on the volunteer efforts of its members to keep it functioning smoothly. In some of my past President's Statements, I have lauded the efforts of our members for their contributions in a variety of capacities. As you know, WSO's Board of Directors, its Committee Chairs and members, and its many other volunteers are a dedicated and talented group and do many things far beyond the call of duty. There is one area, however, that you, the members, need to get involved in: the care and maintenance of the Society's crown jewel—Honey Creek Sanctuary.

Every spring, you may have observed the notices in the *Badger Birder* proclaiming a particular weekend in May as "WSO Annual Work Weekend at Honey Creek." What is this weekend all about and why does WSO need your help with it?

Although most of Honey Creek Sanctuary is managed to preserve its natural features, there are routine, annual maintenance activities that are necessary to allow access by members, but restrict access by cattle. After the ravages of a hard winter or unseasonable weather, fences may need repair to keep cattle out of sensitive stream and wetland habitats, downed trees may need to be cleared from trails, and stream crossings may need to reestablished. This past year for example, saw a major flood remove or damage a significant part of our fences and a snow storm felled many trees across the main trail.

As you may have guessed, the work described above only gets done if someone from our organization volunteers to do it. Because much of the work needs the hands (and backs) of more than one person, the WSO Annual Work Weekend was established to pool volunteers so that work parties would be large enough to handle the bigger jobs. As you also may have guessed, participation in these work weekends has been less than desirable, and the chores have often been handled largely of some of our more senior members.

The work accomplished in this year's and every year's work weekend is important to the long-term enjoyment and preservation of Honey Creek Sanctuary. It is also an opportunity to meet new members, explore the Sanctuary, and really contribute to the well-being of your organization. In keeping with WSO's notable history of outstanding contributions by its members, please consider donating a few hours or a day each May to the upkeep of Honey Creek Sanctuary.

The work weekend for 1993 has been scheduled for May 1 & 2!

President

Eastern Bluebirds *by Frank Mittelstadt.*

Wisconsin Checklist Project: 1992 Update

During 1983–91, project cooperators submitted 45,100 weekly checklists of all birds they saw. The number of cooperators each year declined during this period, but the mean number of species reported on checklists increased. Frequency of occurrence decreased significantly for 18 species but increased significantly for 76 species.

by Robert Rolley

The research committee of the Wisconsin Society for Ornithology (WSO) initiated a research project in 1982 to assess the value of weekly lists of bird species observed by society members for collecting information about Wisconsin's bird species (Temple 1982). Originally, the checklist project was coordinated by staff of the Department of Wildlife Ecology, University of Wisconsin. Temple and Cary (1987) used the checklist records to estimate relative abundance, geographic distribution, and migration chronology of 265 species commonly recorded in the state. Temple and Temple (1986) documented significant correlations between the frequency of occurrence on WSO checklists and independent indices of abundance (Christmas Bird Counts and Cedar Grove Ornithological Station counts) during 4 years for 5 species known a priori to have changed in abundance. Temple and Cary (1990) reported significant positive correlations for 20 species between WSO checklist data and Christmas Bird Counts and positive correlations for 9 species between WSO checklists and U.S Fish and Wildlife Service Breeding Bird Surveys. They concluded that checklist records are useful for monitoring trends in bird populations.

In 1989, responsibility for project administration was transfered to the Wildlife and Forestry Research Section of the Bureau of Research of the Wisconsin DNR. The Department's primary objective for the project is to use the weekly checklists for monitoring long-term changes in abundance of bird species.

METHODS

Checklist project participants were recruited from the membership of the Wisconsin Society for Ornithology. Participants were requested to maintain careful records of the bird species detected each week. Participants recorded their name, the date of the Sunday that began the week, the county in which they birded, whether they "actively " searched for birds during the week, and the bird species detected, on computer readable "bubble forms." Completed forms were mailed to the DNR's Research Center in Monona, Wisconsin. Upon receipt of completed forms, a new supply of forms was mailed to project cooperators. Completed forms were scanned by the University of Wisconsin's Testing and Evaluation Services. Data were transferred to the DNRVAX computer and were analyzed using the Statistical Analysis System (SAS). Trends in reporting frequencies were estimated with linear regression. Trends were classified as stable if the significance level of regressions were ≥ 0.25. Increasing and decreasing trends were considered significant when $P < 0.10$. Checklists from individual counties were grouped into 3 regions (Figure 1) as in Temple and Cary (1987:23).

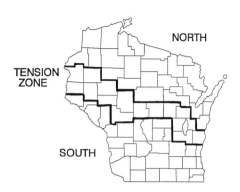

Figure 1. Groupings of counties used for analysis of regional distribution of WSO checklists, after Temple and Cary (1987).

RESULTS

Since initiation of the WSO checklist project, 352 project cooperators have submitted 47,609 checklists. Only the 45,100 checklists for the period 1983–1991 were analyzed for this report. A total of 1,453 checklists have been submitted for years prior to 1983 and 1,056 checklists have been received to date for 1992. The number of cooperators contributing checklists and the number of checklists submitted per year have declined during 1983–1991 (Table 1). As the number of cooperators declined, the percentage of checklists on which contributors indicated that they actively searched for

birds increased. In addition, the mean number of species recorded per checklist increased from 28.4 in 1983 to 32.7 in 1991.

The majority (56.7%) of checklists were from southern Wisconsin, 22.9% were from northern Wisconsin, and 20.4% were from the tension zone. The regional distribution of checklists has changed during 1983–1991 (Table 2). The percentage of checklists from northern Wisconsin increased while the percentage from southern Wisconsin and the tension zone decreased.

Declines in percent occurrence on checklists were noted for 30 species (Table 3). The declines were significant for 18 species: American Bittern, Killdeer, Upland Sandpiper, American Woodcock, Common Nighthawk, Whip-poor-will, Belted Kingfisher, Red-headed Woodpecker, Purple Martin, Barn Swallow, Gray-cheeked Thrush, Brown Thrasher, Vesper Sparrow, Henslow's Sparrow, Bobolink, Western Meadowlark, Common Grackle, and Evening Grosbeak.

Reporting frequencies increased during 1983–91 for 105 species. The increasing trend was significant for 76

Table 1. Number of WSO checklist project cooperators, number of checklists submitted, percent of checklists that represented active birding, and mean number of species reported per checklist during 1983–1991.

Year	No. of cooperators	No. of checklists	% active	Mean no. of species
1983	236	8,524	46.1	28.4
1984	167	6,003	46.6	27.9
1985	142	4,964	41.0	27.9
1986	126	5,169	40.9	28.0
1987	116	5,117	46.0	28.4
1988	110	4,645	44.4	28.8
1989	98	3,685	49.3	29.0
1990	112	3,892	49.4	29.6
1991	76	3,101	53.1	32.7

species. Species exhibiting highly significant ($P < 0.01$) increases included Great Blue Heron, Canada Goose, Wood Duck, Green-winged Teal, Northern Harrier, Sharp-shinned Hawk, Cooper's Hawk, Red-tailed Hawk, American Kestrel, Merlin, Wild Turkey, Sandhill Crane, Least Sandpiper, Ring-billed Gull, Glaucous Gull, Mourning Dove, Red-bellied Woodpecker, Downy Woodpecker, Pileated Woodpecker, Willow Flycatcher, Eastern Phoebe, Black-capped Chickadee, White-breasted Nuthatch, Eastern Bluebird, Yellow-throated Vireo, Northern Cardinal, Savannah Sparrow, Fox Sparrow, and American Goldfinch.

Several species that did not exhibit consistent linear trends during 1983–1991 did show considerable variation in reporting frequencies. For example, percent occurrence of Ruffed Grouse increased from 11.9 in 1983 to a high of 18.7 in 1987 and then declined to 11.1 in 1991. Reporting frequencies for Northern Goshawk declined to a low of 0.6 in 1988 and have subsequently increased.

Changes in reporting frequencies probably reflect changes in population level for most species. However, changes in cooperator activity may contribute to changes in species occurrence of checklists. As the number of cooperators decreased, the percent of active checklists and the number of species reported per checklist increased. This suggests that cooperators who are less active in searching for birds maybe more likely to discontinue contributing checklists. Additionally, changes in regional distribution of checklists likely affects species occurrence. Subsequent analyses of reporting rates will attempt to control for these potentially confounding influences. The future success of this pro-

Table 2. Regional distribution of weekly checklists during 1983–1991.

Year	North	% of checklists Tension zone	South
1983	19.6	24.0	56.4
1984	18.5	19.7	61.9
1985	20.3	20.7	59.0
1986	21.9	21.2	56.9
1987	22.2	20.4	57.4
1988	27.3	20.2	52.4
1989	27.1	17.3	55.7
1990	27.1	18.3	54.6
1991	30.3	16.6	53.1

Table 3. Percentage of WSO checklists on which each species was reported during 1983–1991. Trends were estimated by linear regression analysis.

Species	1983	1984	1985	1986	1987	1988	1989	1990	1991	Trend[1]
Red-throated Loon	0.1	0.1	0.2	0.5	0.5	0.2	0.1	0.0	0.1	stb
Common Loon	6.4	6.6	6.4	5.7	5.9	6.0	6.1	5.4	6.3	dec
Pied-billed Grebe	10.3	10.5	11.0	12.2	12.3	12.3	10.6	7.7	11.9	stb
Horned Grebe	1.9	1.9	1.6	1.8	1.8	1.3	1.4	1.4	1.9	dec
Red-necked Grebe	1.0	0.8	1.0	1.2	1.3	0.8	0.9	0.3	0.5	dec
Double-crested Cormorant	4.7	6.1	5.6	5.4	6.4	6.3	7.0	7.3	12.6	inc**
American Bittern	3.2	3.3	2.7	2.8	2.5	2.6	2.4	2.7	2.7	dec**
Least Bittern	0.7	0.5	0.3	0.9	0.6	0.8	0.8	0.8	0.8	inc
Great Blue Heron	24.2	23.7	28.3	25.1	26.1	27.4	29.4	29.9	35.5	inc***
Great Egret	3.5	4.4	5.0	3.4	3.2	3.7	5.5	4.0	6.9	inc
Cattle Egret	0.4	0.2	0.1	0.1	0.3	0.1	0.3	0.8	0.9	inc*
Green-backed Heron	12.4	10.9	14.5	10.6	10.6	11.7	12.9	12.7	14.7	stb
Black-crowned Night-heron	2.5	2.0	1.3	1.7	1.9	2.4	2.8	3.4	6.3	inc**
Yellow-crowned Night-heron	0.1	0.0	0.0	0.0	0.4	0.0	0.1	0.1	0.2	stb
Tundra Swan	3.8	3.4	3.6	2.7	3.8	3.5	3.8	4.4	4.9	inc*
Mute Swan	2.0	2.0	2.5	2.1	2.7	5.2	3.1	2.4	4.7	inc*
Snow Goose	1.7	2.0	1.5	1.5	1.7	1.7	2.6	2.5	2.4	inc*
Canada Goose	26.7	29.8	29.5	32.7	38.8	41.9	42.6	47.8	52.4	inc***
Wood Duck	14.6	16.6	15.8	15.1	19.2	18.7	17.6	19.5	22.9	inc***
Green-winged Teal	3.5	3.3	3.3	3.7	4.5	4.7	5.2	5.3	8.8	inc***
American Black Duck	7.3	8.2	6.0	7.4	8.1	8.1	10.0	9.1	13.3	inc**
Mallard	51.4	49.1	44.0	48.4	51.9	49.5	52.3	55.3	60.1	inc**
Northern Pintail	3.3	2.0	2.3	2.1	2.8	2.8	3.4	4.0	4.6	inc**
Blue-winged Teal	17.7	15.1	13.7	14.9	14.6	14.6	15.1	14.5	17.1	stb
Northern Shoveler	5.2	4.7	3.5	4.1	3.8	6.5	6.7	6.9	9.0	inc**
Gadwall	2.8	2.9	2.4	2.3	2.3	3.2	3.7	4.2	6.4	inc**
American Wigeon	5.4	3.4	3.4	3.6	4.8	5.5	5.9	5.7	7.9	inc**
Canvasback	3.5	2.4	2.5	2.8	2.9	3.1	3.4	2.9	3.7	inc
Redhead	5.4	3.6	2.3	3.4	3.9	3.7	3.9	3.6	6.6	stb
Ring-necked Duck	6.4	5.7	5.7	5.2	6.9	6.5	8.4	6.6	9.0	inc**
Greater Scaup	5.4	4.6	3.3	4.1	3.4	4.1	4.4	4.2	5.4	stb
Lesser Scaup	10.4	7.6	6.1	7.1	6.9	7.2	8.0	8.5	9.8	stb
Oldsquaw	1.7	1.6	0.8	1.1	0.9	1.3	1.0	1.5	1.8	stb
Black Scoter	0.1	0.1	0.2	0.1	0.2	0.1	0.1	0.1	0.1	stb
Surf Scoter	0.1	0.2	0.2	0.0	0.2	0.2	0.2	0.2	0.0	stb
White-winged Scoter	0.2	0.3	0.2	0.2	0.2	0.3	0.5	0.2	0.3	stb
Common Goldeneye	9.4	9.2	7.2	8.9	8.3	10.1	9.0	9.1	10.7	inc
Bufflehead	8.4	7.3	5.7	6.8	7.0	8.5	9.6	9.0	10.2	inc**
Hooded Merganser	3.6	4.1	2.8	3.7	4.0	5.4	5.5	4.1	6.3	inc**
Common Merganser	6.1	6.1	4.6	6.2	5.7	6.2	6.4	6.6	7.9	inc*
Red-breasted Merganser	5.2	5.9	4.3	4.6	3.9	4.9	5.1	5.3	7.6	stb
Ruddy Duck	6.3	5.2	3.9	5.1	5.3	4.5	5.8	4.6	8.0	stb
Turkey Vulture	8.8	10.5	13.1	10.4	11.7	10.9	10.6	14.0	14.3	inc**
Osprey	3.5	3.8	4.5	3.4	3.3	3.9	3.6	3.1	5.7	stb
Bald Eagle	6.3	7.2	8.0	8.1	8.0	9.6	8.0	7.0	9.9	inc*
Northern Harrier	11.1	11.3	10.3	11.4	13.9	13.9	13.5	13.5	15.4	inc***
Sharp-shinned Hawk	5.2	5.4	6.2	5.8	6.9	7.8	7.4	6.6	9.1	inc***
Cooper's Hawk	3.4	3.6	3.5	4.1	3.8	4.9	6.6	8.2	10.8	inc***
Northern Goshawk	2.1	2.5	1.4	1.4	0.9	0.6	0.9	1.6	2.0	stb
Red-shouldered Hawk	2.4	2.3	2.2	1.8	1.9	2.0	2.0	1.9	2.7	stb
Broad-winged Hawk	6.0	5.1	6.2	5.9	6.0	5.5	3.9	4.8	6.5	stb
Red-tailed Hawk	37.0	40.7	40.9	40.8	44.0	45.0	41.8	44.6	50.6	inc***
Rough-legged Hawk	5.0	6.0	5.5	6.9	9.1	8.0	6.7	7.3	11.0	inc**
American Kestrel	41.1	38.0	39.6	41.2	45.1	45.0	44.3	46.0	51.0	inc***
Merlin	0.7	0.6	0.8	1.1	0.7	0.9	1.2	1.5	1.8	inc***
Peregrine Falcon	0.3	0.3	0.8	0.4	0.4	0.6	0.6	1.4	0.8	inc*
Gray Partridge	2.0	2.2	2.2	2.5	1.8	2.1	2.6	1.4	1.9	stb
Ring-necked Pheasant	20.0	17.1	12.9	12.3	14.2	13.9	15.1	14.7	14.5	dec
Ruffed Grouse	11.9	13.9	13.3	14.6	18.7	17.4	16.9	12.6	11.1	stb
Greater Prairie-chicken	0.9	1.1	0.4	0.4	1.1	1.3	1.4	0.6	1.1	stb
Sharp-tailed Grouse	0.5	0.5	0.9	0.8	0.9	0.5	0.9	0.2	0.2	stb
Wild Turkey	1.0	1.2	1.3	1.9	2.5	3.3	3.8	3.9	7.9	inc***
Northern Bobwhite	2.6	1.6	1.8	1.8	2.2	2.6	2.3	2.2	3.1	inc
Virginia Rail	0.9	0.9	0.9	1.1	1.2	0.9	1.0	0.6	1.3	stb
Sora	3.9	4.7	3.2	3.3	3.6	3.5	3.5	3.9	4.9	stb
Common Moorhen	0.9	0.8	0.5	1.2	1.8	1.2	1.2	0.7	1.5	stb
American Coot	12.1	13.4	11.0	12.3	14.7	12.9	14.4	13.2	16.2	inc**
Sandhill Crane	10.6	11.4	12.4	13.3	15.2	17.8	17.3	18.7	20.1	inc***

(continued)

Table 3. *Continued*

Species	1983	1984	1985	1986	1987	1988	1989	1990	1991	Trend[1]
Black-bellied Plover	0.8	0.9	0.8	0.6	0.9	0.8	1.0	0.8	1.5	inc*
Lesser Golden-plover	0.3	0.3	0.6	0.7	0.6	0.6	0.7	0.5	0.6	inc
Semipalmated Plover	1.3	1.1	1.1	0.9	2.3	2.2	1.5	1.4	2.4	inc
Killdeer	43.1	41.4	43.1	42.2	43.7	40.1	40.3	40.4	40.0	dec**
Greater Yellowlegs	2.7	2.7	3.7	4.2	3.6	4.3	3.9	2.6	3.7	stb
Lesser Yellowlegs	3.7	4.2	5.6	4.9	5.0	5.3	5.5	3.9	5.4	stb
Solitary Sandpiper	2.7	2.7	3.5	2.4	2.6	2.9	2.9	2.7	3.5	stb
Willet	0.2	0.2	0.1	0.1	0.1	0.3	0.1	0.2	0.2	stb
Spotted Sandpiper	7.8	6.7	7.1	5.7	5.7	5.4	5.7	6.3	8.3	stb
Upland Sandpiper	2.1	1.8	1.7	1.7	1.5	1.5	1.5.	1.5	1.7	dec**
Hudsonian Godwit	0.2	0.1	0.2	0.1	0.1	0.4	0.2	0.1	0.0	stb
Marbled Godwit	0.1	0.1	0.0	0.0	0.1	0.2	0.1	0.1	0.1	stb
Ruddy Turnstone	1.0	0.5	0.6	0.6	0.6	0.6	0.4	0.3	1.0	stb
Red Knot	0.2	0.0	0.1	0.2	0.2	0.1	0.0	0.1	0.1	stb
Sanderling	1.0	0.8	1.1	0.6	0.8	0.6	0.8	1.0	0.8	stb
Semipalmated Sandpiper	1.6	1.2	1.7	1.3	2.1	2.2	1.7	2.0	3.2	inc**
Least Sandpiper	1.8	1.6	2.1	1.9	2.6	2.7	2.7	2.6	4.1	inc***
White-rumped Sandpiper	0.2	0.1	0.2	0.3	0.4	0.2	0.2	0.3	0.5	inc
Baird's Sandpiper	0.3	0.3	0.4	0.4	0.8	0.7	0.3	0.5	0.7	inc*
Pectoral Sandpiper	1.8	1.7	2.5	2.4	3.3	3.8	2.3	1.6	4.2	inc
Dunlin	1.7	1.2	1.4	1.3	1.7	1.1	1.2	1.5	3.0	inc
Stilt Sandpiper	0.5	0.3	0.3	0.2	0.7	0.6	0.5	0.2	0.8	stb
Short-billed Dowitcher	1.0	0.9	0.7	0.8	1.6	1.7	1.4	1.3	2.4	inc**
Long-billed Dowitcher	0.3	0.2	0.2	0.4	0.4	0.4	0.3	0.3	0.9	inc*
Common Snipe	0.1	4.9	5.8	7.4	8.3	7.4	7.2	5.0	8.0	inc*
American Woodcock	6.2	5.7	4.9	5.0	5.8	5.1	4.9	3.9	5.0	dec**
Wilson Phalarope	0.8	0.9	0.9	0.6	1.0	1.0	0.8	0.7	1.4	stb
Red-necked Phalarope	0.1	0.1	0.0	0.1	0.2	0.0	0.1	0.2	0.1	inc
Franklin's Gull	0.3	0.3	0.2	0.3	0.1	0.1	0.1	0.2	0.7	stb
Bonaparte's Gull	3.3	4.6	3.2	3.3	3.3	2.8	2.9	3.6	5.2	stb
Ring-billed Gull	17.4	21.3	19.6	21.5	27.1	24.7	27.6	29.9	36.7	inc***
Herring Gull	22.5	21.9	19.2	20.8	19.2	17.0	16.8	22.1	28.8	stb
Glaucous Gull	0.4	0.2	0.2	0.5	0.4	0.4	0.5	0.7	0.9	inc***
Caspian Tern	2.7	2.5	2.2	1.7	1.6	1.9	2.2	4.2	5.0	inc
Common Tern	4.0	3.8	2.6	3.1	2.8	3.1	3.1	3.1	2.8	dec
Forster's Tern	3.0	2.7	1.8	2.2	1.5	1.9	2.3	3.2	4.4	stb
Black Tern	6.3	6.1	5.2	4.8	5.1	5.9	6.1	4.1	5.0	dec
Rock Dove	69.2	72.5	72.2	73.9	73.9	72.3	71.4	70.3	73.8	stb
Mourning Dove	75.3	71.4	74.5	74.7	76.5	79.2	83.8	86.2	89.0	inc***
Black-billed Cuckoo	3.6	3.5	3.2	2.8	4.1	4.8	4.1	3.1	6.2	inc
Yellow-billed Cuckoo	3.0	2.2	1.6	1.3	1.8	3.4	2.2	1.2	2.5	stb
Common Barn-owl	0.1	0.0	0.2	0.0	0.1	0.0	0.0	0.1	0.2	stb
Eastern Screech-owl	2.5	2.7	2.9	2.1	2.5	2.5	2.7	2.5	3.5	stb
Great Horned Owl	10.6	11.7	12.1	11.4	11.4	11.6	12.2	10.2	12.8	stb
Snowy Owl	0.4	0.7	0.3	1.1	1.7	1.1	0.3	0.4	1.2	stb
Barred Owl	9.2	10.9	8.9	9.8	11.2	8.5	8.6	8.7	9.0	stb
Great Grey Owl	0.0	0.0	0.1	0.1	0.0	0.0	0.3	0.0	0.0	stb
Long-eared Owl	0.1	0.4	0.1	0.1	0.2	0.1	0.4	0.1	0.1	stb
Short-eared Owl	0.3	0.5	0.4	0.4	0.3	0.5	0.7	0.4	0.9	inc**
Northern Saw-whet Owl	0.2	0.3	0.4	0.6	0.1	0.2	0.5	0.4	0.3	stb
Common Nighthawk	16.4	15.2	14.6	13.4	13.2	12.0	11.2	9.1	10.7	dec***
Whip-poor-will	6.2	5.8	5.9	5.2	4.3	3.9	4.0	3.9	4.2	dec***
Chimney Swift	23.3	22.0	24.3	21.1	21.5	21.4	21.2	19.9	23.2	stb
Ruby-throated Hummingbird	12.9	11.8	16.2	13.3	11.7	15.7	13.7	14.1	17.6	inc
Belted Kingfisher	23.3	21.8	23.2	21.0	21.0	21.1	21.7	19.7	21.4	dec**
Red-headed Woodpecker	27.5	25.8	22.5	16.5	14.3	12.1	13.0	14.1	13.3	dec***
Red-bellied Woodpecker	20.6	21.7	21.3	25.2	25.2	27.8	28.1	28.8	33.0	inc***
Yellow-belled Sapsucker	7.2	5.2	5.7	6.2	7.1	7.0	6.5	7.2	6.8	stb
Downy Woodpecker	55.3	55.3	59.1	61.4	62.5	65.9	64.6	65.6	68.4	inc***
Hairy Woodpecker	35.1	35.3	39.7	43.0	39.2	41.6	38.3	41.5	44.4	inc**
Northern Flicker	43.8	40.6	41.9	41.9	40.6	40.6	40.7	40.9	43.1	stb
Pileated Woodpecker	10.0	11.6	10.9	11.6	11.8	12.4	12.8	12.7	12.0	inc***
Olive-sided Flycatcher	1.2	0.8	0.5	0.7	0.8	0.7	0.4	0.7	0.6	dec
Eastern Wood-pewee	11.4	12.1	13.7	10.3	11.8	13.1	13.5	11.7	16.9	inc
Yellow-bellied Flycatcher	0.8	0.8	0.9	0.5	0.5	0.5	0.9	0.8	0.6	stb
Acadian Flycatcher	0.5	0.4	0.4	0.2	0.3	0.4	0.3	0.3	0.9	stb
Alder Flycatcher	1.1	1.1	1.2	0.9	0.9	1.1	1.1	1.2	1.9	inc*
Willow Flycatcher	1.3	1.5	1.6	2.2	2.3	2.4	2.9	2.8	3.8	inc**
Least Flycatcher	6.0	4.9	4.5	4.6	4.5	4.4	5.2	5.1	6.3	stb

(*continued*)

Table 3. *Continued*

Species	1983	1984	1985	1986	1987	1988	1989	1990	1991	Trend[1]
Eastern Phoebe	13.4	11.6	11.6	14.2	15.9	15.2	17.9	15.7	18.0	inc***
Great-crested Flycatcher	12.9	11.5	13.6	12.9	13.0	13.7	14.4	13.6	15.4	inc**
Eastern Kingbird	21.3	21.2	24.0	19.8	18.3	20.1	20.3	20.4	21.0	stb
Horned Lark	19.5	20.5	18.2	24.1	19.5	20.0	21.9	18.4	18.5	stb
Purple Martin	15.6	14.7	14.9	13.7	12.1	13.3	12.5	14.7	12.4	dec*
Tree Swallow	33.5	30.7	32.1	31.4	29.1	30.2	28.7	28.4	32.2	dec
Rough-winged Swallow	8.2	7.5	7.3	6.2	6.0	6.7	7.1	7.0	7.4	stb
Bank Swallow	6.4	5.1	5.1	4.3	4.4	3.9	3.1	4.5	5.3	dec
Cliff Swallow	7.6	7.7	8.9	7.4	8.0	8.6	7.5	6.8	8.2	stb
Barn Swallow	30.9	30.5	32.1	29.3	27.8	28.4	28.0	28.3	29.7	dec*
Gray Jay	1.6	2.1	1.4	2.5	2.4	2.1	1.8	1.2	0.5	dec
Blue Jay	80.6	84.6	86.4	85.2	81.2	82.2	81.0	82.8	85.1	stb
American Crow	85.0	87.9	87.3	90.4	89.1	89.3	89.3	88.5	91.3	inc**
Common Raven	7.9	10.4	10.8	12.7	12.3	11.3	10.8	10.0	9.5	stb
Black-capped Chickadee	71.8	75.0	78.5	81.6	80.0	82.7	81.1	83.3	85.4	inc***
Boreal Chickadee	0.2	0.1	0.1	0.3	0.3	0.1	0.3	0.1	0.2	stb
Tufted Titmouse	3.1	3.6	3.9	3.7	4.5	5.8	4.2	2.1	2.7	stb
Red-breasted Nuthatch	15.3	13.1	17.8	14.0	16.1	13.6	23.0	28.3	16.1	inc
White-breasted Nuthatch	59.1	59.9	64.2	65.7	63.7	65.2	64.0	65.9	66.5	inc***
Brown Creeper	9.9	8.6	6.4	6.8	7.7	9.3	9.7	8.6	9.8	stb
House Wren	23.8	23.1	26.3	25.6	23.6	21.0	24.6	25.8	28.1	stb
Winter Wren	2.8	2.3	1.8	2.0	2.3	2.0	2.7	2.5	3.8	inc
Sedge Wren	3.0	3.8	3.1	3.9	4.3	3.9	3.3	3.0	3.6	stb
Marsh Wren	3.9	3.0	2.7	3.1	3.1	3.2	3.1	3.4	5.3	inc
Golden-crowned Kinglet	7.7	5.6	5.5	6.1	6.9	6.8	6.9	7.6	8.8	inc*
Ruby-crowned Kinglet	8.3	7.6	6.2	7.0	5.8	6.6	8.3	6.9	9.6	stb
Blue-gray Gnatcatcher	3.1	3.0	3.1	2.5	3.1	2.8	4.2	3.8	5.9	inc**
Eastern Bluebird	14.3	13.7	17.2	19.2	23.3	23.7	25.3	28.5	30.7	inc***
Veery	6.3	5.0	4.8	4.2	4.0	4.1	3.7	4.1	6.0	stb
Gray-cheeked Thrush	2.8	2.4	1.0	0.9	0.7	1.0	1.0	1.1	1.4	dec*
Swainson Thrush	5.6	4.2	2.9	3.0	2.7	2.8	2.8	3.3	4.5	stb
Hermit Thrush	5.7	4.4	4.0	5.1	4.6	4.1	5.4	5.3	7.4	inc
Wood Thrush	7.4	6.7	7.8	7.1	7.4	7.2	7.7	7.4	7.8	inc
American Robin	71.5	65.8	68.2	64.6	64.8	64.8	65.4	67.6	67.7	stb
Gray Catbird	26.5	25.9	28.5	23.6	24.3	23.9	25.7	25.4	28.8	stb
Northern Mockingbird	0.2	0.3	0.1	0.1	0.3	0.1	0.0	0.2	0.1	stb
Brown Thrasher	19.9	19.2	18.2	17.1	16.5	15.8	15.6	15.2	16.7	dec***
Water Pipit	0.3	0.2	0.4	0.5	0.2	0.3	0.6	0.2	0.5	stb
Bohemian Waxwing	0.3	0.7	0.6	0.9	0.6	1.1	0.8	0.6	0.3	stb
Cedar Waxwing	26.3	31.7	32.4	26.9	25.4	25.8	29.1	28.9	29.1	stb
Northern Shrike	1.9	2.7	4.1	4.8	3.4	3.6	3.0	3.0	4.0	stb
Loggerhead Shrike	0.4	0.2	0.7	0.2	0.2	0.3	0.5	0.2	0.2	stb
European Starling	81.1	80.5	78.9	83.7	81.5	79.1	80.0	79.1	81.3	stb
Bell's Vireo	0.2	0.0	0.1	0.0	0.1	0.0	0.0	0.3	0.5	inc
Solitary Vireo	1.9	1.6	1.0	1.0	0.9	1.0	1.1	1.7	2.0	stb
Yellow-throated Vireo	2.7	2.2	2.6	2.3	2.5	2.8	4.2	3.6	5.0	inc***
Warbling Vireo	6.3	6.0	6.4	5.8	6.2	6.4	7.3	6.9	8.6	inc**
Philadelphia Vireo	1.5	1.3	0.6	0.9	1.2	1.1	0.9	1.5	1.5	stb
Red-eyed Vireo	9.9	8.8	10.5	9.8	10.4	10.4	10.7	10.6	14.6	inc**
Blue-winged Warbler	1.7	1.9	2.0	2.0	2.3	2.6	3.2	2.0	2.8	inc**
Golden-winged Warbler	2.2	1.7	1.3	1.4	1.5	1.8	1.6	2.0	2.5	stb
Tennessee Warbler	4.2	2.9	3.2	3.4	4.2	3.2	3.6	3.2	5.9	stb
Orange-crowned Warbler	1.7	1.2	0.8	0.9	0.9	1.2	1.1	1.1	1.8	stb
Nashville Warbler	5.8	4.6	3.5	4.2	3.0	2.8	3.7	3.4	5.3	stb
Northern Parula	1.6	1.3	0.7	0.8	0.8	1.2	1.0	1.3	2.0	stb
Yellow Warbler	12.2	9.5	8.8	8.9	9.1	9.3	10.8	10.8	12.1	stb
Chestnut-Sided Warbler	5.7	4.6	4.1	3.5	3.7	4.7	3.9	4.7	5.7	stb
Magnolia Warbler	5.6	4.2	3.2	3.3	2.9	3.1	3.6	4.2	5.4	stb
Cape May Warbler	2.4	1.4	1.2	1.9	1.7	1.7	1.8	1.6	2.5	stb
Black-throated Blue Warbler	1.1	0.5	0.3	0.5	0.4	0.6	0.4	0.6	0.9	stb
Yellow-rumped Warbler	12.2	11.1	9.9	11.8	11.7	11.4	12.6	12.6	14.9	inc**
Black-throated Green Warbler	5.5	4.1	3.6	2.9	2.9	3.0	3.6	4.1	5.5	stb
Blackburnian Warbler	3.9	2.5	1.7	1.8	1.6	2.0	2.3	2.8	2.7	stb
Pine Warbler	1.4	1.4	1.2	1.3	1.1	0.8	1.0	1.9	3.0	inc
Palm Warbler	5.3	5.0	4.4	4.1	3.8	3.9	4.9	5.1	5.9	stb
Bay-breasted Warbler	2.5	1.8	1.3	1.3	1.3	1.7	1.4	1.6	2.5	stb
Blackpoll Warbler	2.4	2.1	0.9	1.0	1.1	1.3	1.4	1.4	2.9	stb
Cerulean Warbler	0.5	0.5	0.3	0.4	0.6	0.5	0.4	0.6	0.9	inc

(continued)

Table 3. *Continued*

Species	1983	1984	1985	1986	1987	1988	1989	1990	1991	Trend[1]
Black-and-white Warbler	5.9	5.0	3.7	3.8	3.3	4.2	5.3	5.2	6.4	stb
American Redstart	9.6	7.3	7.2	5.7	5.9	6.7	7.8	8.2	10.8	stb
Prothonotary Warbler	0.5	0.7	0.2	0.3	0.4	0.3	0.5	0.4	0.4	stb
Ovenbird	9.4	7.6	8.8	8.0	7.7	8.4	8.4	8.7	10.0	stb
Northern Waterthrush	4.0	3.2	2.7	1.9	2.1	2.0	2.6	2.8	3.5	stb
Louisiana Waterthrush	0.5	0.4	0.6	0.5	0.4	0.4	0.4	0.4	0.7	stb
Kentucky Warbler	0.2	0.1	0.1	0.3	0.3	0.2	0.3	0.2	0.4	inc**
Connecticut Warbler	0.8	0.7	0.5	0.5	0.5	0.5	0.7	0.4	0.6	dec
Mourning Warbler	2.2	1.8	1.7	1.7	1.6	1.6	1.9	1.8	2.4	stb
Common Yellowthroat	17.7	17.1	17.4	15.9	14.7	15.2	16.1	15.2	18.8	stb
Hooded Warbler	0.3	0.2	0.2	0.1	0.2	0.3	0.1	0.3	0.1	stb
Wilson's Warbler	3.1	2.6	1.2	1.2	0.8	1.5	1.4	2.1	2.2	stb
Canada Warbler	2.5	2.0	1.0	1.1	0.9	1.3	1.6	1.7	2.3	stb
Yellow-breasted Chat	0.3	0.2	0.2	0.1	0.2	0.2	0.1	0.2	0.2	stb
Scarlet Tanager	5.7	4.3	4.7	5.1	4.7	5.5	6.1	5.6	8.6	inc**
Northern Cardinal	63.0	65.7	66.3	67.6	67.5	67.6	69.1	72.8	76.2	inc***
Rose-breasted Grosbeak	17.4	15.1	17.5	15.4	15.5	16.2	17.8	18.1	20.8	inc*
Indigo Bunting	16.2	15.7	16.9	12.9	13.3	13.3	14.4	14.6	16.3	stb
Dickcissel	0.7	0.4	0.2	0.3	1.0	2.2	1.7	1.3	2.6	inc**
Rufous-sided Towhee	10.9	11.8	10.5	10.4	11.1	10.2	10.1	8.8	11.6	stb
American Tree Sparrow	20.4	17.9	15.5	15.7	13.7	17.1	19.1	20.9	21.3	stb
Chipping Sparrow	27.2	26.1	28.9	27.7	26.7	26.9	28.6	28.7	32.5	inc*
Clay-colored Sparrow	2.3	2.2	1.9	2.7	2.4	2.6	2.4	2.3	3.1	inc*
Field Sparrow	14.2	13.3	12.8	13.2	15.2	13.8	15.1	12.9	15.9	inc
Vesper Sparrow	7.9	8.8	8.3	6.9	6.1	6.8	6.8	6.1	5.9	dec***
Lark Sparrow	0.1	0.2	0.2	0.2	0.2	0.2	0.2	0.5	0.4	inc**
Savannah Sparrow	8.9	9.4	9.2	10.2	10.0	10.1	11.2	10.5	12.0	inc***
Grasshopper Sparrow	1.7	1.4	1.6	1.6	1.6	1.0	1.7	1.8	3.4	inc
Henslow's Sparrow	1.0	0.9	0.9	0.8	0.9	0.5	0.3	0.2	0.5	dec***
Le Conte's Sparrow	0.3	0.3	0.2	0.3	0.3	0.3	0.2	0.5	0.8	inc*
Fox Sparrow	5.1	4.0	4.5	4.6	6.2	6.4	6.4	6.1	8.7	inc***
Song Sparrow	42.1	38.1	37.8	38.1	40.7	39.7	42.4	42.2	46.7	inc*
Lincoln's Sparrow	1.9	1.6	1.4	1.3	1.2	1.1	1.5	1.4	2.5	stb
Swamp Sparrow	8.8	9.5	8.3	8.1	8.7	7.9	9.0	8.8	12.8	inc
White-throated Sparrow	14.5	17.0	13.7	13.4	13.8	13.0	14.9	15.3	18.8	stb
White-crowned Sparrow	5.0	4.6	3.3	4.2	2.9	3.4	3.4	4.6	4.7	stb
Harris' Sparrow	0.2	0.8	0.8	0.3	0.6	0.5	0.5	0.7	0.1	stb
Dark-eyed Junco	43.4	44.4	39.0	45.2	42.8	44.5	42.5	43.2	46.0	stb
Lapland Longspur	0.8	0.7	1.0	1.4	1.7	1.1	0.8	0.9	1.4	stb
Snow Bunting	2.9	3.1	3.6	4.8	3.5	4.5	4.6	2.6	3.1	stb
Bobolink	9.1	8.3	9.1	7.5	7.3	7.5	7.4	6.1	7.7	dec**
Red-winged Blackbird	58.6	54.4	54.8	51.7	52.6	51.3	50.6	55.9	56.3	stb
Eastern Meadowlark	30.0	25.5	25.1	25.9	26.1	24.1	23.7	25.2	28.4	stb
Western Meadowlark	9.3	7.7	7.2	8.9	7.1	6.1	6.9	5.0	5.6	dec***
Yellow-headed Blackbird	4.5	3.8	2.9	4.0	4.6	4.4	5.3	3.8	4.8	stb
Rusty Blackbird	2.1	2.2	2.1	2.9	2.8	2.7	2.7	1.7	3.0	stb
Brewer's Blackbird	6.1	6.3	6.4	8.5	6.7	5.8	4.9	6.7	7.3	stb
Common Grackle	61.4	55.2	55.9	53.8	53.6	52.5	51.6	52.8	53.4	dec**
Brown-headed Cowbird	28.3	24.2	24.5	26.7	25.7	26.2	26.4	27.8	29.3	inc
Orchard Oriole	0.6	0.6	0.5	0.6	0.4	0.4	0.4	0.4	0.8	stb
Northern Oriole	21.0	18.7	19.9	18.0	17.2	18.8	19.2	18.6	19.1	stb
Pine Grosbeak	0.2	0.7	3.5	3.3	0.8	1.1	2.0	4.1	0.5	stb
Purple Finch	21.6	21.7	22.8	23.0	22.7	23.4	19.7	23.9	22.4	stb
Red Crossbill	0.4	1.0	2.6	0.4	1.1	3.0	0.2	0.9	0.5	stb
White-winged Crossbill	0.1	0.2	0.4	0.1	0.8	0.7	1.5	2.6	0.1	inc
Common Redpoll	0.3	3.5	2.5	7.9	4.7	4.7	2.8	7.7	2.7	stb
Pine Siskin	5.0	16.3	13.1	15.4	25.9	29.1	13.5	33.3	8.1	stb
American Goldfinch	68.9	72.1	74.2	71.7	72.4	76.4	74.1	77.2	76.9	inc***
Evening Grosbeak	9.5	13.3	14.3	18.3	11.3	9.2	5.7	7.1	5.8	dec*
House Finch[2]									18.9	
House Sparrow	83.0	84.7	84.5	86.3	84.3	82.3	83.9	82.2	82.3	dec

[1]stb = stable: regression equations with P $\geq$ 0.25, inc = increasing: regression equations with positive slopes and P < 0.25, dec = decreasing: regression equations with negative slopes and P < 0.25. * = 0.10 > P $\geq$ 0.05, ** = 0.05 > P $\geq$ 0.01, *** = P < 0.01.

[2]House Finch was not included on WSO checklists until 1991.

ject in monitoring of bird population levels will be dependent on retaining existing and recruiting new cooperators.

LITERATURE CITED

Temple, S. A. 1982. A Wisconsin bird survey based on field checklist information: a WSO research project. *Passenger Pigeon* 44:56–60.

Temple, S. A. and J. R. Cary. 1987. *Wisconsin birds: a seasonal and geographical guide.* University of Wisconsin Press, Madison, WI. 364pp.

Temple, S. A. and J. R. Cary. 1990. Using checklist records to reveal trends in bird populations. Pp. 98–104. *In* J. R. Sauer and S. Droege, eds. Survey design and statistical methods for estimation of avian population trends. *U.S. Fish Wildl. Serv., Biol. Rep.* 90(1).

Temple, S. A. and A. J. Temple. 1986. Year-to-year changes in the abundance of Wisconsin birds: results of the WSO checklist project. *Passenger Pigeon* 48:158–162.

Robert Rolley
Bureau of Research
Wisconsin DNR
Monona, WI

50 Years Ago in *The Passenger Pigeon*

From the report of the business meeting held in April 1942 in Green Bay: "Other important business transacted at the meeting was the incorporation of the Society and correction of the constitution with such major changes and the addition of Life and Patron members and a new name of The Wisconsin Society for Ornithology, Inc. It was voted to change the period of publication of the Society's bulletin THE PASSENGER PIGEON from monthly to quarterly, to erect the proposed Passenger Pigeon monument at Wyalusing State Park near the confluence of the Mississippi and Wisconsin Rivers, and to hold the next annual meeting of the Society in April 1943 in Waukesha under the auspices of the Benjamin F. Goss Bird Club."

Before it (business meeting) was over, Mr. E. W. Strehlow had paid his $25 fee to the Treasurer, thereby making him the first Life Member of the Society. (Excerpts from Volume 4, 1942)

Trends in Waterfowl Use of University Bay, Lake Mendota, Wisconsin (1947–80)

Fall waterfowl use of University Bay on Lake Mendota in south-central Wisconsin was recorded from 1947–1980. The purpose of this study was to determine the value of the University Bay to waterfowl and to relate changes in waterfowl distribution and abundance to changes in the environment and to continental and flyway population levels. Environmental changes included eutrophication and increased turbidity of the lake due to agriculture and rapid urbanization in its watershed. These led to changes in vegetation composition and abundance, and limited data suggest an associated reduction in invertebrate abundance and diversity. Additionally, rapid urbanization resulted in increased human activity resulting in waterfowl disturbance.

by William J. Vander Zouwen

Migrating waterfowl traditionally stop in wetlands that consistently supply a safe resting place and food to replenish depleted energy reserves. Many of these wetlands have experienced increasing eutrophication, siltation, and recreational use. Until more is known about the relationship between waterfowl and these changes in stopover areas, management of such wetlands as waterfowl habitat is handicapped.

The objective of this study was to describe the fall waterfowl use of a southern Wisconsin wetland over a long period of time, in order to provide a case history of waterfowl response to changing environmental conditions.

I analyzed 33 years of observations of the fall waterfowl use of University Bay on Lake Mendota. I address: 1) characteristics of waterfowl use of the wetland and adjacent areas, 2) environmental changes on the wetland, and 3) trends in waterfowl abundance and spatial distribution in relation to local environmental changes and regional trends in waterfowl abundance.

STUDY AREA

Lake Mendota is one of a chain of 5 eutrophic hard-water lakes in the Yahara River drainage basin of Dane County, Wisconsin (Fig. 1). The city of Madison and its suburbs surround the 3941-ha lake. The 106-ha University Bay on the south side of the lake gained refuge status on 22 September 1944, following a series of 9 land acquisitions by the University of Wisconsin between 1866 and 1941 (Dillon 1956). Hereafter, I refer to University Bay as the Bay.

The Bay is bounded by the University of Wisconsin to the south, Nielsen Marsh to the west, the Picnic Point peninsula to the north, and the open lake to the east (Fig. 2). Willow Creek and a pumping-station channel are the only 2 inlets.

The Bay is characterized by a 21-ha shallow-water shelf separated by a gravel bar from the deeper eastern portion where maximum depth is 16 m. Also, a narrow shallow-water shelf

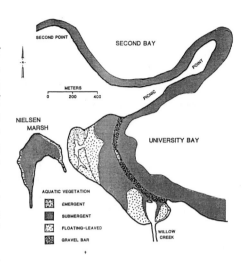

Figure 2. Aquatic vegetation of University Bay, Second Bay, and Nielsen Marsh in 1980.

is followed by a sharp drop-off into deeper water along the south side of Picnic Point. Silt and plant detritus form the bottom west of the bar; a gradation from sand to black gyttja occurs to the east into deep water. Two emergent and 2 floating-leaved aquatic plant communities exist, but submerged vegetation dominates the Bay (Fig. 2).

Extensive development on adjacent land has taken places since the 1940's. Where only cropland, fields, and woods bordered the Bay in 1949, several University buildings, a parking lot, and athletic fields now exist. Most of those closest to the Bay were constructed between 1959 and 1967. Additionally, student apartment complexes were built northwest of the Bay in the late 1950's and early 1960's.

The storm sewer outfall of a rapidly growing commercial and residential area was placed at the head of Willow Creek in 1948 (Ahern 1976). The drainage basin of Willow Creek enlarged from less than 8 km² to greater

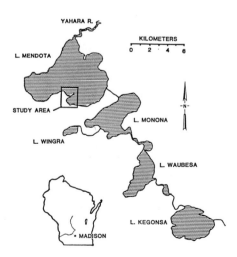

Figure 1. Study area location in chain of lakes in Madison, Wisconsin metropolitan area.

than 15 km² in the late 1950's and early 1960's (Sterrett 1975), the period of greatest urban growth in that area. In the early 1970's this 822-ha watershed was 86% residential and 14% commercial; over 25% was covered by impervious surfaces (Ahern 1976). Increased real estate development surrounding the Bay and Lake Mendota between 1950 and 1980 resulted in part from increased University enrollment and population growth in the city of Madison.

Hunting has not been permitted on the Bay since the initiation of the study in 1946, but it is a multiple-use area. Uses of the Bay include fishing, pleasure boating, practice drills by the University rowing team, research, nature observation, and mooring of boats and a pontoon plane. Considerable vehicular and pedestrian traffic occur on adjacent roads and paths.

Second Bay, located to the north of the Picnic Point peninsula (Fig. 2), was added to our study area in 1959. It is an open, relatively deep bay (most >2 m). Aquatic vegetation consisted of a strip of submergents along shore, and the entire shoreline remained wooded throughout the study. The owner of part of the land bordering Second Bay has hunted waterfowl there.

A large marsh, west of the Bay, was drained between 1910 and 1920 (Dillon 1956) and farmed, primarily for corn. Drainage tiling began to fail in the early 1960's. Consequently a small marsh reformed in 1966, at which time it was included in our study area. By 1968 the marsh grew to 12 ha, but land-fill activities reduced it to 5.7 ha by 1970. Nielsen Marsh, as it is called, had a maximum depth of 0.5 m in 1980, and water levels have been controlled by a pumping station.

METHODS

Census Procedures—Each year since 1946, a graduate student was responsible for monitoring and reporting on the waterfowl use of the University Bay during fall migration. The reports and records of each student were filed and formed the basis for this paper. All species of Anatidae, American Coots, and Common Loons using the Bay refuge were censused.

Census initiation and termination dates varied among years; the former ranged from 16 September to 6 October, and the latter ranged from 1 December to 4 January. Surveys were usually terminated when the Bay became ice-covered. The census schedule was generally 3 counts weekly. Only in 1951 was the number of counts per week less than 2. Observers stopped at several observation stations, scanned each area with a spotting scope, and recorded all waterfowl present. Morning counts were conducted in all but 2 years, usually beginning within 1 hour of sunrise. Each count lasted between 45 minutes and 2.5 hours depending on the number of waterfowl present and whether Second Bay and Nielsen Marsh were included.

Analysis—I chose duck-use days between 1 October and the last count of each year as the best measure of waterfowl use of the study area that could be compared among years. Duck-use days was calculated by interpolating between counts to assign a number to dates without a count and then adding counts for all dates. Records from 1946 and 1949 could not be used because of insufficient data.

Linear-regression analyses were conducted using data from 33 years for the most important species and species groups to determine if significant trends existed. In addition to individual species, diving ducks, dabbling ducks, Mallards and Black Ducks, and other dabblers were grouped for some analyses.

In the years 1968–1980, the distribution of waterfowl on the Bay was mapped using similar zones (Fig. 3). Prior to 1968, some reports provided only general descriptions and maps of distribution plotted by other methods. Trends in duck distribution on the Bay were determined by comparing these early reports with more recent zone-data.

RESULTS AND DISCUSSION

Waterfowl Use—Many species of waterfowl stopped at the Bay each year during fall migration. Coots, loons, and 19 species of Anatidae were common (Table 1). Pied-billed Grebes and

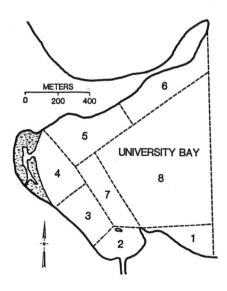

Figure 3. Zones of University Bay used to map distribution.

Horned Grebes also frequented the Bay but were not included in the census in many years. The coot was the most abundant species, accounting for 72% of waterfowl use of the Bay. Among ducks, dabblers comprised 76% of use. The most abundant were Mallard, Black Duck, American Wigeon, and Gadwall. Canvasback, Bufflehead, Hooded Merganser, Greater Scaup, Lesser Scaup, and Redhead were the most common diving ducks. Scoters (*Melanitta* sp.), Oldsquaw, Tundra Swan, Snow Geese, White-fronted Geese, Red-breasted Merganser, and Double-crested Cormorant were rare visitors, together comprising less than 1% of total use. An average of 300 ducks and 754 coots per day used University Bay from 1 October to freeze-up during the 33-year period.

The Bay was an important part of the Madison lakes system for waterfowl. Aerial surveys revealed that Lake Mendota accounted for an average of 91% of the duck use of the 3 most important Madison lakes in 1951–1954 (Dillon 1956). Within Lake Mendota, the Bay was unique in having diverse and abundant vegetation together with large areas of both shallow and deep water. Additionally, protection from north and west winds made the Bay attractive to divers, dabblers, and coots alike. The attractiveness of the Bay to such a large number of species is attested to because all duck species known to frequent Wisconsin (Jahn and Hunt 1964) used the Bay. During 1954–1956 the species composition was surprisingly similar (Table 2).

Seventeen species of Anatidae, coots, and loons visited Second Bay during the study (Table 1). The American Coot was the dominant species, comprising 73% of total waterfowl use.

Table 1. Numbers and percentages of duck-use days of species of waterfowl using University Bay, Second Bay, and Nielsen Marsh[1].

Species/Group	University Bay		Second Bay		Nielsen Marsh	
	No.	%	No.	%	No.	%
Canvasback	2,101	8	809	19	4	<1
Ring-necked Duck	1,051	4	435	10	6	<1
"Scaup"	539	2	107	3	4	<1
Redhead	488	2	56	1	5	<1
Bufflehead	1,316	5	442	10	45	<1
American Goldeneye	720	3	254	6	5	<1
Hooded Merganser	602	2	46	1	1	<1
Common Merganser	138	1	325	8	0	0
Ruddy Duck	95	<1	17	<1	8	<1
Other Divers	4	<1	0	0	0	0
Divers, Total	6,154	25	2,491	59	78	1
Mallard	11,039	44	1,371	32	4,823	51
Black Duck	3,704	15	287	7	292	3
American Wigeon	1,720	7	39	1	1,133	12
Gadwall	1,565	6	23	1	1,811	19
Northern Shoveler	253	1	1	<1	414	7
Green-winged Teal	170	1	1	<1	414	4
Blue-winged Teal	34	<1	0	0	106	1
Northern Pintail	76	<1	1	<1	45	<1
Dabblers, Total	18,561	75	1,723	41	9,327	99
Wood Duck	149	1	40	1	29	<1
Canada Goose	41	<1	0	0	0	0
Anatidae Total	24,905	28	4,254	26	9,434	79
American Coot	62,597	72	11,810	73	2,513	21
Common Loon	20	1	19	1	0	0

[1]University Bay, Second Bay, and Nielsen Marsh data represent the periods 1947–1980, 1959–1980, and 1968–1980, respectively.

However, unlike the Bay, diver use was greater than dabbler use. Diving duck species composition was similar to that in the Bay, except that Common Mergansers were more common on Second Bay. Mallards and Black Ducks accounted for 96% of the dabbling duck use of Second Bay.

Nielsen Marsh, adjacent to the Bay and part of the refuge, primarily attracted dabbling ducks (99% of duck use). Mallards, Gadwalls, and American Wigeons were commonly observed there (Table 1). Coot use was second only to Mallard use but comprised a smaller proportion of the total use in Nielsen Marsh than in the other 2 areas. An average of 221 waterfowl per day were present. In some years peak numbers approached 700.

Large numbers of coots were usually present by 1 October (Fig. 4). Peak numbers occurred in mid–October and numbers tapered off until December, when few remained. The Blue-winged Teal was the earliest migrant on the study area; peak numbers were usually present before 1 October. American Wigeons, Gadwalls, Green-winged Teal, Northern Shovelers, and Northern Pintail were also usually present by 1 October (Fig. 4), but peak numbers occurred between mid–October and mid–November. Few remained into early December, although open water was available.

Table 2. Comparison of species composition of waterfowl use of Wisconsin and University Bay (1954–1956).

Species	Wisconsin[1]	University Bay
Mallard	30%	48%
Black Duck	7%	15%
American Wigeon	20%	2%
Gadwall	Tr	2%
Northern Shoveler	Tr	Tr
Green-winged Teal	Tr	Tr
Blue-winged Teal	4%	Tr
Northern Pintail	3%	Tr
Wood Duck	Tr	Tr
Dabblers	64%	68%
Canvasback	14%	12%
Ring-necked Duck	10%	6%
Redhead	3%	2%
"Scaup"	8%	2%
Bufflehead	Tr	7%
Common Goldeneye	1%	Tr
Mergansers	Tr	Tr
Ruddy Duck	Tr	Tr
Divers	36%	32%
Coots	44%[2]	54%[2]

[1]From Jahn and Hunt (1964).
[2]Percent of total duck and coot use.

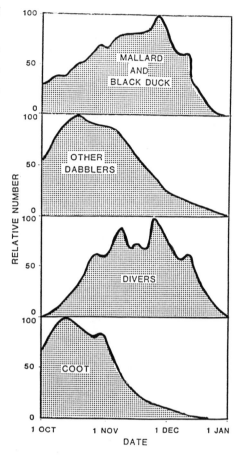

Figure 4. Chronology of use of University Bay refuge by Mallard and Black Duck, other dabblers, coot, and divers. Peak count is given value of 100.

Mallards and Black Duck were also present by early October. Many, however, were urban ducks which are present year-round. Highest numbers occurred from early November to early December (Fig. 4), later than the other dabbler species. Mallards and Black Ducks often concentrated on Lake Mendota and the Bay in late November and early December when most other shallow, smaller wetlands in the Madison area were ice-covered. For example, in 1980 over 48% of the Mallard and Black Duck use of the Bay occurred in the last week of open water; as many as 1700 Mallards and 130 Black Ducks were present.

Diver use of the Bay was highest between late October and mid–December (Fig. 4). Few were present prior to 1 October, and many were often pres-ent until freeze-up in December. Red-heads, Ring-necked Ducks, and Ruddy Ducks were the earliest arrivals (Table 3); the former 2 species accounted for most of the early diver use. Scaup, Buf-flehead, Hooded Merganser, and Can-vasback numbers built up next. Canvasbacks and scaup often re-mained relatively abundant until freeze-up. American Goldeneyes and Common Mergansers were the latest users of the Bay; peak numbers occurred during the 2 weeks preceding freeze-up.

The overall chronology of use in the Bay area by most waterfowl was similar to the chronology of migration of these same species through this region as shown by Jahn and Hunt (1964) and Bellrose (1976). However, use of the Bay was somewhat later and more prolonged than those investigators indicated for Mallard, Black Duck, Canvasback, scaup, mergansers, and Common Goldeneye. This difference emphasizes the importance of the Bay and Lake Mendota as a late-season waterfowl-use site. Most of the shallower, smaller, and more northern lakes of Wisconsin become ice-covered before Lake Mendota does (Bunge and Bryson 1956). Although duck use in the state has declined by late November and early December, Lake Mendota still received substantial use. Many of these late migrants remain as far north as conditions permit (Bellrose 1976). Jahn and Hunt (1964) noted that most of the canvasback remaining in Wisconsin into December were present on 2 southern lakes, Lake Geneva and Lake Mendota. Mallards and Black Ducks are special cases; they have not depended on food resources on the refuge but make feeding flights to surrounding fields, loafing during the day on available open water. The presence of a resident population perhaps decoyed wild birds and prolonged the use of the refuge.

Coot and diver use was highest in the Bay throughout the fall where vegetation was much more extensive. The proportion of coot use occurring in Second Bay increased from early October (9%) to early November (33%). Apparently, newly arriving coots preferred the Bay to Second Bay, but as numbers increased, there was a spillover into Second Bay (Fig. 5). Food supplies in the Bay may have been depleted. The similar diver shift during this period was likely a result of decoying by coots as well as food supply changes.

In early autumn, dabblers preferred Nielsen Marsh to the Bay probably due to the denser vegetation and higher proportion of desirable food plants in the marsh. All of the water area was less than 0.5 m, within the depth range prescribed as ideal for dabbling ducks by the Atlantic Flyway Council (1972). By late November vegetation in Nielsen Marsh diminished, and the marsh became ice-covered. Relative use there decreased to 0% from 55% for Mallards and Black Ducks and from 76% for other dabblers, while relative use of the Bay increased.

Within the Bay, coot and diver use of zones west of the bar (2, 3, 4, and

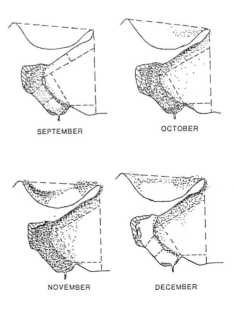

SEPTEMBER   OCTOBER

NOVEMBER   DECEMBER

Figure 5. Fall monthly distribution changes of coot on University and Second Bays (1964).

5) decreased, while use of zones east of the bar (6 and 8) increased as the season progressed (Fig. 6). The area west of the bar froze over earliest making food inaccessible. Moreover, like Andrews (1946), we observed that vegetation in the shallow water, particularly west of the bar, decayed earlier than vegetation in deeper water such as along Picnic Point (zone 6).

Relative Mallard and Black Duck use of the northwest area of the Bay (zones 4 and 5) increased to a high (44% and 23%, respectively) in November while use of the southwest area (zones 2 and 3) declined (Fig. 6). In addition to the late freeze-up of the former, more migrants were present in November (based on number of these ducks relative to other times of the year), which were more likely to use the northwest area due to lesser human activity. The relative use of the ice-free shallow zones (1 and 6) east of the bar increased in December. Here, Mallards and Black Ducks fed on wave-deposited vegetation and often dove for food in water up to 1.5 m deep.

Monthly changes in distribution of other dabblers on the Bay were similar to that of Mallards and Black Ducks, except that relative use of the northwest area (zones 4 and 5) remained high in December (15 to 30% and 38%, respectively) (Fig. 6). Most of these dabblers remained only as long as this area was ice-free and, then, left the Bay rather than shift to other zones. Thus, loss of food source and confinement by ice were the prime factors regulating monthly dabbler distribution on the Bay.

Habitat Changes—Annual variation and trends in waterfowl use of a wetland are governed in part by changes in habitat. It is, therefore, essential to describe habitat changes, including eutrophication, siltation, vegetation, invertebrates, adjacent areas, and human activity, in order to explain changes in waterfowl use during the 33-year study.

Changes in the Lake Mendota drainage basin, including rapid urbanization of Madison, rapid growth of towns upstream, farm activity, and drainage of large acreages of wetlands in the basin, were suggested as causes of dramatic increases in nutrient levels and sedimentation in the Bay and Lake Mendota beginning in the 1940's (Bortleson and Lee 1972, Sterrett 1975, Ahern 1976). Additionally, silt and nutrient input to the Bay probably increased substantially in the late 1950's and early 1960's, following channelization of Willow Creek in 1957 and the rapid urbanization of its watershed (Fig. 7).

In 1974 alone, after most construction and related erosion had eased, 353,000 kg of total suspended solids and 922 kg of total phosphorus entered the Bay via the creek; these loadings were shown to be capable of producing eutrophic conditions and substantial siltation in the Bay (Ahern 1976). Willow Creek's silt load was great enough to create an island in its delta, where depth was previously 0.5–1.5 m. The area of the delta less than 0.1 m deep increased 350% during the last 7 years alone. Sedimentation was not confined to this area; rather, it covers much of the Bay. During field work in 1980, a silt covering was particularly evident on vegetation west of the bar.

The most apparent and, perhaps, most important change directly affecting waterfowl was that of aquatic vegetation. Following increases in

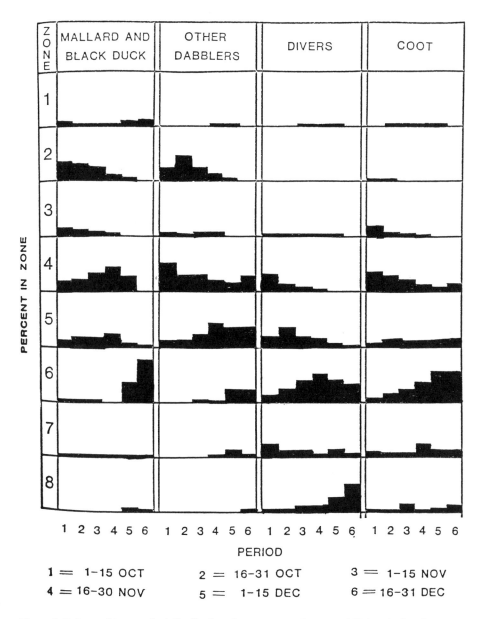

Figure 6. Fall monthly waterfowl distribution changes among 8 zones of University Bay for 1968–1980.

nutrients and suspended matter, the species composition and distribution of aquatic macrophytes began to change. At the onset of this study, 21 aquatic macrophytes were found, com-

pared to 17 and 14 in 1966 and 1980, respectively (Andrews 1946, Lind and Cottam 1969, Vander Zouwen 1982). Five pondweeds (*Potamogeton* sp.), water crowfoot (*Ranunculus trichophyl-*

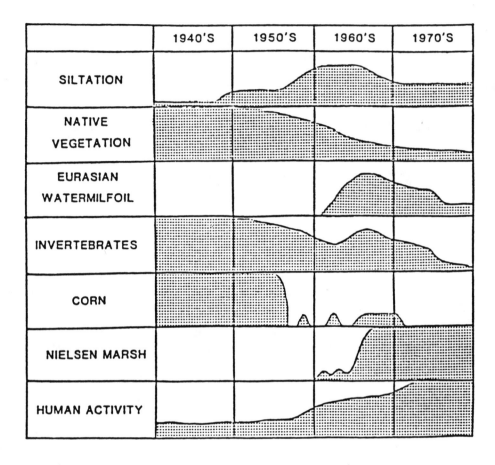

Figure 7. Conceptualization of habitat changes in and around University Bay refuge (1940–1980).

lus), spadderdock (*Nuphar* sp.), muskgrass (*Chara* sp.), and northern watermilfoil (*Myriophyllum exalbescens*) have disappeared; exotics and turbidity-tolerant species became dominant. The most dramatic losses of native vegetation occurred in the late 1950's and early 1960's following large-scale construction in the Willow Creek watershed (Fig. 7).

When censuses began in the 1940's, wild celery (*Vallisneria americana*), coontail (*Ceratophyllum demersum*), pondweeds, and muskgrass were the predominant submergent species (An-

drews 1946). Three dense softstem bullrush (*Scirpus validus*) beds on the bar protected the submerged vegetation to the west from excessive wave action. Dense growths of floating-leaved plants supported mats of duckweed (*Lemna* sp.) at each end of the Bay.

By 1966 many of the pondweeds had disappeared, muskgrass was scarce, and the near uniform distribution of wild celery had been reduced to a strip along the bar and Picnic Point (Lind and Cottam 1969). Eurasian watermilfoil (*Myriophyllum spicatum*), an exotic, became the dominant species over most of the Bay. The watermilfoil explosion probably occurred between 1962 and 1966 (Carpenter 1979). Coontail continued to be abundant into the early 1970's.

Typical of watermilfoil invasions elsewhere, it declined after about 10 years of abundance and remained at low levels since 1976 (Fig. 7) (Carpenter 1979). By 1980 mats of duckweed were absent, coontail was scarce, bullrush persisted sparsely in only 1 stand, and the 1966 distribution of wild celery was reduced by one-half (Vander Zouwen 1982). Submergent vegetation in general became sparse over much of the Bay. The vegetative decline and silt deposition caused further adverse effects due to increased turbidity from resuspension of sediments by wave and rough-fish action.

Vegetation, found in dense beds to 5–7 m deep in the 1940's, was largely limited to water depths less than 2 m by 1980. The reduction in maximum depth of vegetation resulted in a plant distribution closer to shore; approximately a 30% reduction in vegetated area (Vander Zouwen 1982). It was this deep water segment that persisted intact late into November while vegetation in water less than 2 m disintegrated (Andrews 1946). In addition, the large masses of fruits and plant fragments that wave-action piled up along shore at the onset of this study no longer occurred.

Invertebrates were abundant and diverse in the Bay in the 1940's (Andrews 1946). Unfortunately, there have been no subsequent similar studies of invertebrate abundance in the Bay. However, the large hatches of midges (Chironimidae), mayflies (Ephemeroptera) and caddis flies (Trichoptera) that occurred up to the late 1950's are now absent.

Invertebrate abundance may have begun to decline in the late 1950's with the reduction in native vegetation (Fig. 7). However, the invasion and subsequent dominance by Eurasian watermilfoil may have initially resulted in increased invertebrate abundance. Krecker (1939) found that this species held larger numbers of invertebrates compared to many other plant species. Andrews and Hasler (1943) similarly found relatively high invertebrate abundance on a closely related species, northern watermilfoil (*Myriophyllum exalbescens*), in the Bay. Krull (1970), however, found that Eurasian watermilfoil held the least invertebrate biomass and numbers for 12 macrophytes studied in New York.

Siltation and nutrient enrichment typically results in decreased invertebrate diversity and abundance; Trichopera, Ephemeroptera, Odonata, and Mollusca are usually lost, and chironomids, tubificids, and nematodes usually remain (McGaha 1952, Paloumpis and Starret 1960, Mills et al. 1966, Jonassen 1969, Morgan 1970). Moreover, invertebrates are usually much more abundant in vegetated than nonvegetated areas (Moyle 1961, Krull 1970). Schroeder (1973) suggested that extensive reduction in plant species abundance and diversity should be avoided if invertebrate diversity and abundance are to be maintained. These findings together with the lack of substantial insect hatches on the Bay leads us to assume that invertebrates have been greatly reduced, particularly in the last decade accompanying the drastic vegetative decline.

Second Bay changed similarly to University Bay. Vegetation was found in water depths less than 25 m and was predominantly Eurasian watermilfoil and wild celery in 1980. Wild celery and pondweeds were dominant and present to a greater depth earlier (Denniston 1921).

A large cornfield was located adjacent to the Bay until 1956. From 1957 to 1970 smaller plots were planted in some but not all years. No corn was planted there after 1970.

The Nielsen Marsh area became a temporarily flooded area dominated by smartweeds (*Polygonum* sp.) and grasses in the early 1960's. From 1966 to 1972 it was a shallow marsh dominated by bullrush (*Scirpus* sp.). High water levels and a muskrat (*Ondatra zibethicus*) population (>100 lodges) reduced the emergent vegetation to a narrow strip along shore by 1973, creating an open water situation that prevailed through 1980. In 1974 Nielsen Marsh was dry from July through the first week of October, when it was filled by heavy rains. Low water levels occurred in 1975–1977, particularly in 1976 when only a few puddles existed. The drawdown was followed by stable water levels occurred during 1978–1980, resulting in production of a large biomass of food in the form of submergents (pondweeds, horned pondweed *Zannichellia palustris*, and coontail), duckweed, and associated invertebrates.

Human activity is part of the environment that affects waterfowl use of the Bay. For example, on 6 and 9 November 1954, 2200 and 950 ducks, respectively, departed the Bay when a fisherman motored through the area used by waterfowl. In past years some contributors to this study indicated that boats were regularly present. In 5 years that disturbance was recorded,

human activity resulted in departure of ducks in the following percentages of observation periods: 44% in 1953; 27% in 1957; 32% in 1960; 33% in 1964; and 43% in 1973.

Human activity on and around the Bay has increased. Shore activity increased substantially since the 1950's due to development of land adjacent to the Bay for housing, parking, athletic fields, offices, labs, and classrooms, together with a higher human population. The dramatic increase in jogging, beginning in the early 1970's, resulted in increased human activity not only along the south and west shores but also on the Picnic Point peninsula on the north shore of the Bay. Fishermen and boaters were reported as the major disturbance factor of the 1950's (Dillon 1956). During the last decade the University rowing team has been cited as the major disturbance factor. Their boats were present every morning at dawn, traversing the Bay in drills. Although the rowing team used the Bay as early as the early 1900's, it appears that their use has increased. Not until the 1970's was this activity considered by observers to be the major disturbance factor. Crew disturbance has not replaced, but rather added to other boating disturbance. Furthermore, fishing and other boating activity have also increased with a growing Madison population.

Trends in Distribution—Detailed comparisons of waterfowl distribution during the 1970's with earlier years cannot be precise, because those data are not as complete; however, comparisons do reflect general trends in distribution. In order to understand distributional changes in the use of the Bay, it will be necessary to consult the area map and to be familiar with its component parts (Fig. 3).

In the 1950's the greatest concentrations of Mallards and Black Ducks (ca 65%), other dabblers (ca 95%), divers (ca 45%), and American Coots (ca 80%), occurred in the northwest area (zones 4 and 5) of the Bay (Fig. 8). Of the divers, Redheads and Ring-necked Ducks used this area almost exclusively, and when disturbed usually returned. For example, in 1954, 100–600 ring-necked Ducks actively fed there for nearly 2 weeks. Abundant food together with abundant loafing sites, shallow water depths (most <1.0 m), and minimal human activity, made this area attractive to all waterfowl.

Relative use of the northwest area by all waterfowl declined in the 1960's (Fig. 8) concurrent with changes in species composition of aquatic vegetation. The expanded waterfowl distribution was likely due primarily to the replacement of native vegetation by the exotic, Eurasian watermilfoil. Apparently this species was less suitable as food, because waterfowl were rarely observed feeding on it. For example, whereas coots were observed feeding primarily on pondweeds, coontail, and wild celery in the 1950's and primarily on coontail in the 1960's and early 1970's, we observed them feeding on filamentous algae associated with watermilfoil (but not on watermilfoil) in the late 1970's when little coontail was present. Florschutz (1972) also recorded Eurasian watermilfoil as receiving little use by coot in Currituck Sound, North Carolina and Back Bay, Virginia following invasion by this exotic. Perhaps, the reduction in food supply necessitated use of a larger portion of the Bay in order to obtain adequate quantities of food.

The use of zones other than the northwest area was especially evident late in the year, perhaps due to exhaustion of the less abundant food in that area.

Following reduction in submergent vegetation, duckweed, and channel and mudflat size, relative use of this area declined to 35% for Mallards and Black Ducks, 45% for other dabblers, 23% for divers, and 50% for coots. Reduced food supplies discouraged dabbler and coot use and resulted in reduced decoying and the security of numbers, probably accounting for decreased use of this area by divers.

The second greatest concentration of Mallards and Black Ducks (ca 25%) in the 1950's occurred in the area at the mouth of Willow Creek (zone 2) where loafing sites on mudflats were abundant. Although this area had diverse vegetation, little feeding occurred there. Early observers believed that these ducks were Madison residents because of their calm nature and consistent number. Few other waterfowl species used this area. Although sedimentation formed additional loafing sites in the form of an island, relative use of this area by Mallards and Black Ducks decreased slightly from the 1950's (25%) to the 1970's (20%). This lower use, in spite of the apparently improved habitat, was due to the reduction in number of resident Black Ducks in Madison. Few adults or broods have been seen in recent years compared with earlier decades. Perhaps as Figley and VanDruff (1982) pointed out, Black Ducks were not as tolerant of urbanization (i.e., human activity and habitat change) as Mallards.

The increased relative use of this area by the other dabbler group from the 1950's (<5%) to the 1970's (37%)

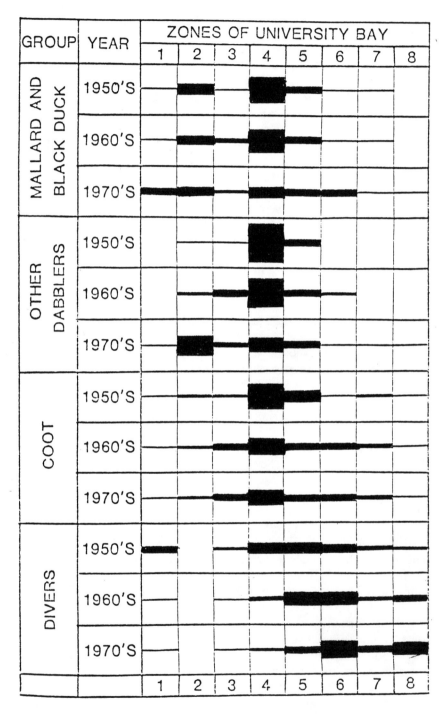

Figure 8. Mallard and Black Duck, other dabbler, coot, and diver distribution in University Bay in 1950's, 1960's and 1970's.

was likely due more to the decline in suitability of the northwest area than increased attractiveness. The aquatic plant community of the Willow Creek-mouth area was reduced both in area and diversity due to sedimentation, yet a small area of watermilfoil, coontail, wild celery, and pondweeds remained. Most of the Gadwalls, wigeons, teal, and shovelers were associated with this bed of aquatic plants.

The Picnic Point area (zone 6) was primarily used by divers (15–20% of diver use), especially late in the year, as well as a small proportion of the coots (<5%) in the 1950's. Relative use of this area began to increase in the 1960's, and by the 1970's, 38% of divers, 16% of coot, and 15% of Mallards and Black Ducks were observed there. Increased relative use by divers and coots was likely due to the lesser effect of turbidity and silt on vegetation there than in shallow water west of the bar. Sediments, during the extensive construction in the watershed in the 1950's, progressed northward toward Picnic Point immediately after heavy rains. Siltation was therefore greatest at the mouth of the creek and least along the south shore of Picnic Point. The habitat in the Picnic Point area had not improved, but was degraded at a lesser rate than other areas of the Bay. Additionally, the proximity of this area to escape habitat (open lake) may have been important to divers because of increasing human activity on and around the Bay. Food conditions probably do not explain increased relative use of the Picnic Point area by Mallards and Black Ducks, because the water is greater than 0.5 m deep. Recently, greatest Mallard and Black Duck concentrations occurred on the Bay late in the year, when other Mad-

ison area waters as well as the west area of the Bay were ice-covered. At this time the Picnic Point area was the shallowest, most sheltered ice-free part of the Bay.

Common Goldeneyes, scaup, Canvasbacks, and Buffleheads were commonly observed in the area along the south shore of the Bay (zone 1) in the 1950's. For example, 80% of the scaup in 1952 and 40% of the Canvasbacks in 1957 were observed here. University dormitories were constructed along the south shore in the late 1950's. Consequently, relative diver use decreased from about 15% in the 1950's to less than 5% in the 1960's and 1970's. Apparently this was caused by increased human activity, because an attractive bed of wild celery remained through the 1960's and 1970's. Thornburg (1973) similarly found abandonment of areas with abundant food due to disturbance.

Increased use of the south shore area by Mallards and Black Ducks in the 1970's (<5% to 14%) may, similar to the Picnic Point area, relate to the presence of large numbers late in the year. A water discharge pipe maintained an area free of ice that these dabblers used in late November and December.

Most of the outer bay area (zone 8) was deep enough to preclude macrophyte growth and consequently received little waterfowl use in the 1950's (Fig. 8). However, relative diver use of this area increased from about 5% to 24% by the 1970's. Because this area had negligible vegetation and divers there were usually loafing rather than feeding, I believe that increased use was due to its distance from human activity on shore. Cornelius (1977) and Cronan (1957) also suggested that the distribution of Redheads in Luguna Madre, Texas and scaup in Connecticut, respectively, was influenced by human activity.

During the 1950's Second Bay received little use by waterfowl. Divers were present for only short periods, often when boats disturbed ducks on the Bay or strong south winds occurred. University Bay received more than 75% of the diver use of the 2 bays during all but 2 years (1960 and 1961) during the period 1959–1969. Relatively high use of Second Bay in these 2 years was due to the presence of large concentrations for a short time; 66% and 72% of those observed in 1960 and 1961, respectively, occurred on just 2 consecutive counts. Diver use of the Bay relative to Second Bay declined from greater than 75% of use to less than 15% in 1979 and 1980. Similarly, relative coot use of the Bay declined from near 100% in the early 1960's to 50% in 1980. Because change in distribution of divers and coot was gradual and did not occur in the mid-1960's, it was not correlated with the sudden change in species composition of vegetation in the Bay. Little feeding occurred on Second Bay by most waterfowl. Indeed, the same vegetation changes had occurred in Second Bay. Rather, the trend likely reflected the gradual decline in all vegetation together with increased human activity on the Bay. Thompson (1973) and Thornburg (1973) similarly found diurnal concentrations of loafing ducks in areas of the Keokuk Pool, Mississippi River that had relatively low food supplies but had the security of low disturbance.

No trend occurred in relative use of Second Bay by dabblers. In all years but 1961, more than 78% of dabbler use of the 2 bays occurred on the Bay. Although the Bay habitat changed, the paucity of loafing sites, shallow water foods, and shelter apparently discouraged dabbler use of Second Bay.

Morning and evening flights to the Nielsen Marsh area when it was a cornfield originated from the Bay and other Madison waters. Often, 200–500 Mallards and Black Ducks fed on waste corn and the manure spread on the field. Pintails that used areas of the lake other than the Bay were also attracted to the field. In the early 1960's when part of the field was too wet for crop production, many Mallards and Black Ducks, and some Gadwalls, American Wigeons, Northern Shovelers, and teal fed on the waste corn, grasses, and smartweeds following rains that created temporary pools. On several occasions over 1,000 ducks were observed feeding there.

By 1968, this periodically flooded field became a 12 ha marsh dominated by bullrush, that received 32% and 44% of the study area use by Mallards and Black Ducks and other dabblers, respectively. Many waterfowl species were observed feeding, however, many Mallards and Black Ducks only loafed there and visited the nearby cornfield in morning and evening. In addition to its use as a day feeding and loafing site, large numbers of ducks flew into the marsh at dusk to roost in the emergent vegetation and on muskrat lodges.

The loss of emergents in 1973 resulted in lower relative use of Nielsen Marsh only for coot (Fig. 9). I did not expect this to occur, because open water allows for growth of submergent foods.

As early October rains filled the dry marsh in 1974, ducks immediately be-

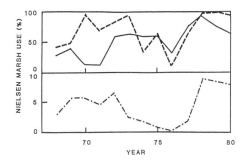

Figure 9. Yearly relative use of Nielsen Marsh and University Bay by Mallard and Black Duck (solid), other dabblers (dashed), and coot (dash-dot) (1968–1980).

gan using the area, probably feeding on the flooded moist-soil plants such as smartweeds. However, the flooding was too late to provide growths of submergents and duckweed, which Gadwalls and American Wigeons prefer (Munro 1949, Stewart 1962, Jahn and Hunt 1964, Cowardin 1969, White and James 1978); consequently relative use of Nielsen Marsh by the other dabbler group was low (35%) (Fig. 9). Ninety percent of the Green-winged Teal use of the study area was still in Nielsen Marsh, probably due to the flooding in areas of preferred food in the form of seed-bearing weeds (Olney 1963, Bellrose 1976).

In 1976, when Nielsen Marsh was reduced to a few large puddles, relative Mallard and Black Duck use was lower than several previous and later years, and relative use of the marsh by the other dabbler group (12%) and coot (1%) was lower than in any other year (Fig. 9).

Following these dry years (1974–1977), high water levels during 1978–1980 resulted in the production of a large biomass of food. Gadwalls and American Wigeons fed so consistently

on duckweed that their distribution corresponded with duckweed mat distribution. In these 3 years, higher Mallard and Black Duck, other dabbler, and coot use of the study area occurred in Nielsen Marsh (80%, 97%, and 8%, respectively) than in any previous year (Fig. 9). Without the emergents and muskrat lodges, ducks used the marsh for feeding and loafing only during the day. At dusk, all ducks left, presumably for areas with good roost sites.

In 1979 and 1980, 75% and 79%, respectively, of the October diver use of the study area was on Nielsen Marsh. In 1980 a flock of 10 to 22 Buffleheads was present every day for 3 weeks during late October and November. Most of the divers using the marsh not only loafed but actively fed there. They, too, became acclimated to human activity in a short time. Human activity at the same proximity on the Bay (where few dabblers were present) brought about diver departure.

Besides vegetation and water level conditions, the length of time Nielsen Marsh remained ice-free influenced the amount of use it received. Many ducks, particularly Mallards, Gadwalls, American Wigeons, and Shovelers, remained on the marsh until it froze over. The use of the marsh by both Mallards and other dabblers was correlated with the number of days of open water in October and November for 1968 to 1977. Exceptional food supply and water level conditions in 1978–1980 resulted in a similar relationship, but at an elevated level of use.

Relative use of Nielsen Marsh by Mallards and Black Ducks increased, but no apparent trend occurred in relative use by the other dabblers and coot (Fig. 9). Rather, relative use of Nielsen Marsh appeared to fluctuate depending on ambient conditions. For its size, Nielsen Marsh received a disproportionately large amount of the refuge use.

Trends in Diver Abundance— Changes in waterfowl use of the Bay are a function of both local conditions and waterfowl population size in general. Yearly use of the Bay may be influenced by variation in weather conditions, food quality and biomass, and human activity that were not measured. Further, I recognize inherent problems in using some of the population indices we have chosen as indicators of population change (e.g., weather and hunting regulations affect proportion of population harvested; fall population levels reflect production as well as breeding population size; overall population size may change while numbers crossing Wisconsin do not, or vice versa).

Because little comparable population information is available for years prior to 1955, I will limit our discussion largely to 1955–1980. Nielsen Marsh use is combined with Bay use to describe dabbler trends, because dabblers may have used the Bay had Nielsen Marsh not been present.

Consistently high Ring-necked Duck use occurred through 1956; very low use was recorded in 1957 and use fluctuated through 1980, usually below pre -1957 levels (Vander Zouwen 1983). Use was particularly low in the last 5 years (avg. = 85 duck-use days).

Canvasback use of the Bay remained high from 1954 to 1961. High use occurred again in 1964 and 1965, but use remained low thereafter (avg. =

291 duck-use days) (Vander Zouwen 1983).

Although Redhead use of the Bay fluctuated in the 1950's it was higher in most of those years than any thereafter (Vander Zouwen 1983). A decline occurred primarily in the early to mid-1960's. After 1963, average use was only 117 duck-use days.

Excluding 1953 and 1954, when unusually high use occurred, scaup use of the Bay changed relatively little (Vander Zouwen 1983). However, scaup was lower in 5 of the last 10 years than in any previous year. Although scaup were not identified to species, most were probably Lesser Scaup because a much larger number of this species than Greater Scaup migrate across Wisconsin (Bellrose 1976).

Like the divers previously discussed, Bufflehead use declined from the mid-1950's to the late 1970's. Average use for 1976–1980 (403 duck-use days) was lower than that for any previous 5 year period (Vander Zouwen 1983). Although there have been high-use years throughout the period, there were more low use years later than earlier.

Common Goldeneye use of the Bay declined steadily, if the unusual year 1974 is not included (Vander Zouwen 1983). During 8 of the last 10 years, the Bay received less Goldeneye use than all but one previous year (Vander Zouwen 1983).

Use of the Bay by Hooded Mergansers was relatively low in the 1950's and 1970's, increased 8-fold in the mid-1960's, and then declined as rapidly (Vander Zouwen 1983). Unfortunately, little is known about the status of this species. Nevertheless, an increase of this magnitude would not likely have occurred in the Hooded

Merganser population, particularly at a time when bottomland habitat was disappearing (Bellrose 1976). Moreover, I observed as many as 100 Hooded Mergansers on nearby Lake Wingra in 1979 and 1980, when none were present on the Bay. Therefore, this species still migrated through the Madison area but no longer used the Bay as it once did.

Several divers showed an increased use from the onset of our study to the mid-1950's. Explanations for this increase phase include mid-day censuses, general population increases, and changes in local conditions. The mid-day counts in 1947 and 1948 may partially explain such low recorded use in those years, because many divers depart the Bay by noon due to disturbance. I cannot, however, offer this as an explanation for 1950–1952, because only early morning counts were conducted. Water conditions on the prairie,pothole region improved considerably during this time (Kiel et al. 1972). Hawkins (1964:191) stated "During the mid-fifties waterfowl populations built up to the highest levels of recent times . . ." Unfortunately, there is a paucity of comparable population information for the years before 1955. However, aerial surveys revealed an increase in diver use of Madison lakes between 1951 and 1954, and a review of *Audubon Field Notes* from the "Western Great Lakes Region" indicated a generally increasing fall waterfowl flight from the late 1940's to the mid-1950's (Dillon 1956). The increased duck use of the Bay was likely due in part to these population increases. However, even species breeding in more stable habitat, such as Ring-necked Duck, scaup, and

Bufflehead (Bellrose 1976), showed an increased use of the Bay.

Local conditions may have also been responsible for the increased use of the Bay. The drastic increase in nutrient levels in Lake Mendota beginning in the 1940's (Bortleson and Lee 1972) may have caused increased macrophyte productivity and thus increased food that could have attracted and held larger numbers of ducks. However, macrophytes were abundant in the lake earlier (Denniston 1921). Also, a comparison of Bay census records with aerial counts of Lake Mendota waterfowl (Jahn and Hunt 1964) revealed that large numbers of divers were on the lake relative to the Bay in the early 1950's. Large concentrations of canvasback were located at the north end of the lake where extensive beds of wild celery, sago pondweed (*Potamogeton pectinatus*), and coontail occurred (Denniston 1921). We speculate that vegetation in this area would have been the first to be affected by excessive amounts of nutrients and silt, causing turbidity. This area is at the mouth of the Yahara River, which drained a watershed to the north with extensive agricultural land and growing towns. The Bay, far from this inlet and whose watershed had not yet been altered dramatically, may have then attracted these divers.

Use of the Bay by species traditionally known to feed primarily on vegetation (e.g., Canvasbacks, Redheads, and Ring-necked Ducks) declined earliest and most dramatically.

Ring-necked Duck use was usually much lower from 1957 to 1980 than earlier. It was in 1957 that Willow Creek was channelized, removing the filtering effects of a marsh at its mouth. Moreover, construction in the rapidly growing, urbanizing Willow Creek watershed at this time increased turbidity in the Bay. Of the plant species available in the Bay, the seeds of pondweeds are most well known as a food of Ring-necked Ducks (Cottam 1939, Mendall 1958, Anderson 1959). The northern pondweeds, abundant in the 1940's (Andrews 1946) and 1950's (Dillon 1956), are highly turbidity intolerant (Davis and Brinson 1980) and probably began declining at this time. In addition, aquatic plants may respond to poor water conditions by reducing fruit production (Low and Bellrose 1944). The loss of pondweeds and their fruits, that likely occurred, may account for the decline of Ring-necked Duck use, because population indices do not explain the decline. Use of the Illinois River Valley similarly decreased concurrent with a vegetation decline (Mills et al. 1966).

Canvasback and Redhead use declined next. These species traditionally favored tubers, leaves, and stems of wild celery, pondweeds, and muskgrass (Cottam 1939, Anderson 1959, Stewart 1962). Concurrent with the Canvasback and Redhead decline (early to mid-1960's) was the reduction of these plant species and replacement by a nearly monotypic Eurasian watermilfoil community. Apparently, this vegetation was unsuitable for these divers, because the drastic decline in use did not parallel population changes. Bergman (1973) found that extensive beds of vegetation influenced selection of staging lakes in Canada. The same is likely true for migration stopover areas as well. Redhead use of Spring and Peoria Lakes in the Illinois River Valley also decreased following a vegetation decline (Mills et al. 1966). Similarly, a vegetation decline in Chesapeake Bay

was followed by reduced Redhead and Canvasback use (Perry et al. 1981).

Use of the Bay by diving duck species that feed primarily on invertebrates, namely Goldeneyes, Buffleheads, and scaup (Cottam 1939, Stewart 1962, Rogers and Korschgen 1966, Erskine 1972) also declined but more gradually. There was no sharp decline in use with change in aquatic vegetation species composition. Other investigators (Mills et al. 1966, Perry et al. 1981) noted that some species that fed predominantly on invertebrates were little affected by loss of submergent vegetation. Invertebrates associated with watermilfoil as well as chironomids and tubificids that are commonly present in the muds of eutrophic and polluted waters may have been a primary food supply. Ruddy Ducks in Chesapeake Bay (Perry et al. 1981) and Tufted Ducks (*Aythya fuligula*) in Europe (Morgan 1970) shifted to this food source with vegetative decline or eutrophication. However, invertebrate food in the Bay likely declined due to siltation as well as vegetative decline, particularly evident since 1975. Bufflehead, goldeneye, and scaup use was lowest after 1975. Habitat changes probably caused the decreased use by these divers, particularly the Bufflehead whose Bay use trend differed so radically from continental population trends.

In recent years, Canvasback diet changed to an invertebrate base in areas lacking suitable vegetation (Thompson 1973, Perry et al. 1981), although they still fed on vegetation where it was abundant such as Lake Onalaska, Wisconsin of the Mississippi River (C. Korschgen pers. commun.). Perhaps the invertebrates that Canvasback feed on (primarily molluscs) have not survived the siltation or vegetative decline of the Bay or never were abundant.

Like its trend in Bay use, food habits of Hooded Mergansers are most different of divers so far discussed. A large proportion of its diet is fish, in addition to crustaceans and insects (Cottam and Uhler 1937, Stewart 1962). I can only speculate that the changes in species composition of aquatic vegetation initially supported higher populations of these animals or made them more vulnerable to predation. The subsequent decline in vegetation would result in less cover, and thus lower populations of suitable fishes and invertebrates, possibly explaining the decline in Hooded Merganser use.

In addition to changes in food quantity, increased disturbance was likely responsible in part for the diving duck use decline on the Bay. Disturbance affected diver use more than dabbler or coot use. Human activity on or near the Bay usually resulted in diver departure. Moreover, because most of the dabblers used Nielsen Marsh rather than the Bay, less decoying and security in the Bay would have resulted. Thus, disturbance may have had an added effect on divers in the 1970's.

Several observers reported that ducks took flight but returned following disturbance in the 1950's, the return of disturbed divers was rare in the 1970's. Probably the reduction in food reduced the attractiveness of the Bay such that divers would not return if disturbed. Migration behavior changes may have affected use of the refuge. Divers appear to have increased concentration on fewer areas, including the Mississippi River, overflying the rest due to habitat degradation and disturbance such as has occurred on the Bay. Although there is little evidence for migration route shifts due to non-local factors such as breeding ground conditions and winter habitat conditions, this explanation cannot be ruled out. However, I observed thousands of divers migrating over but not landing on Lake Mendota in recent years. Further, a lake the size of the Bay, just a few kilometers away, held 200–300 divers for a few weeks in recent years, even though at least 4 groups of hunters were present most days; this area did have abundant vegetation. At the same time, the Bay received little use.

A combination of all of these factors was likely responsible for the decline in diver use of the refuge. However, local conditions, especially vegetative change and disturbance, were probably the most important factors.

Trends in Dabbler Abundance—Mallard use of the Bay increased to the mid-1950's and decreased thereafter (Vander Zouwen 1983). The trend in use of Nielsen Marsh was similar. Changes in mallard use of the Bay refuge probably reflected changes in general continental and flyway population levels.

Black Duck use has declined steadily since the late 1940's (Vander Zouwen 1983). The addition of Nielsen Marsh Black Duck use did not alter the trend.

American Wigeon use of the Bay was usually between 1000 and 4000 duck-use days, being highest in the late 1940's, early 1950's, and early 1960's (Vander Zouwen 1983). Following 1969, the Bay had very little wigeon use. When high use occurred, it was on Nielsen Marsh.

Gadwall use of the Bay remained low through the early 1960's, at which time use increased substantially (Vander Zouwen 1983). Madison Christmas Bird Counts also showed this increase (Vander Zouwen 1983). Bay use fluctuated markedly during the remainder of the period, ranging from 20 duck-days use in 1972 to 7159 in 1980. Unlike American Wigeon, Gadwall made extensive use of the Bay in a few years of the last decade.

Like Gadwall use, Bay refuge use by shovelers increased (Vander Zouwen 1983). High use occurred from the mid-1960's on. In some years, refuge use was nearly 10 times greater than the average use prior to the mid-1960's. Peak use of the Bay occurred in the mid-1960's. Thereafter, most use occurred in Nielsen Marsh, but high use occurred on the Bay in 1974 and in 1976. Except for these 2 years, use of the Bay was lower in the 1970's than in any previous year.

The termination of corn planting adjacent to the Bay may have had an effect on study area use by Mallards and Black Ducks, the 2 species which commonly fed there. However, several factors confound this relationship. The planting of corn was not abruptly halted. Rather, plots became smaller and were planted in some but not all years between 1957 and 1970. When corn was not present, these fields were still fertilized with manure where Mallards and Black Ducks fed on undigested corn. Moreover, corn was present on farms within a short distance of the Bay (less than 5 km), well within their feeding-flight range (Jahn and Hunt 1964), when corn adjacent to the Bay was absent. Corn was still planted within 15 km of the Bay at the end of the study. Nevertheless, the amount of corn adjacent to the Bay declined, and at the same time Mallard and Black Duck use declined. The decline in Black Duck use probably reflects general population decline rather than refuge habitat change. Mallards now feed in Nielsen Marsh whereas they obtained food in the cornfields in early years. However, the loss of corn may have affected use of the Bay, because the Madison winter mallard population increased (Table 4) while refuge use remained relatively stable.

The reduction of native aquatic vegetation and replacement by Eurasian watermilfoil did not, initially, adversely affect dabbler use of the Bay. Indeed, use by wigeon, Shoveler, and Gadwall was higher in the 1960's than in previous years. Either the remaining native vegetation was adequate or their diets switched to watermilfoil. Because increased use coincided with increases in population indices, I cannot determine to what degree each of these factors brought about increased use of the Bay.

Within a few years of the vegetation changes, use of the Bay by these dabblers declined in favor of Nielsen Marsh use. Very low Bay use occurred in the 1970's. Whether this was due to attractiveness of Nielsen Marsh, unattractiveness of the Bay, or both is not known. However, the loss of duckweed, and reduction of coontail, wild celery, pondweeds, and even watermilfoil in the 1970's must have reduced the Bay's attractiveness. Moreover, the favored loafing area along the cattail mash was reduced, and the vegetation decline led to increased wave action, reducing suitability of shallow water areas for loafing.

Another indication that the Bay became less attractive was the change in chronology of use by Gadwall and American Wigeon. In the 1950's and 1960's Gadwall and American Wigeon used the refuge much later than in the 1970's (Vander Zouwen 1983). It appears that in the 1970's, when most of these ducks used Nielsen Marsh, they left the study area rather than shift to the Bay when Nielsen Marsh froze. The longer stay of these 2 species in the 1950's and 1960's was likely due to later freeze-up in the shallows of the Bay, better food supply in the Bay, and many more divers, from which Gadwalls and American Wigeons commonly stole food when shallow areas were ice-covered.

Whereas Wigeons were not abundant on the Bay in any year in the 1970's, Gadwall and Shovelers used the Bay to a large extent when conditions were unfavorable on Nielsen Marsh (1974–1976). Perhaps the Gadwall's habit of feeding on filamentous algae in the absence of suitable macrophytes allowed them to find sufficient food in the Bay. The diverse food habits of Shovelers allowed them to remain in abundance when poor vegetative conditions occurred. Bellrose (1976) observed that Shovelers were abundant on lakes largely devoid of macrophytes that had abundant plankton. I also observed shovelers feeding on the abundant plankton in the Bay.

Human activity probably had less effect on dabbler numbers than diver numbers, because they were more tolerant. However, the increased human activity together with sparse food apparently contributed to the low use of the Bay in recent years.

Whether the Bay refuge use by dabblers would be as high without Nielsen Marsh is moot. However, dabblers ob-

viously preferred Nielsen Marsh, an area much smaller than the Bay with greater proximity to human activity. If the Bay were as suitable in the 1970's as earlier years, larger numbers would have used the Bay and not Nielsen Marsh alone. I believe that Bay refuge use by dabblers, like divers, would have declined drastically had it not been for the reclamation of Nielsen Marsh.

Trends in Coot Abundance—Coot use of the Bay did not change from the 1940's to the 1970's. Use fluctuations were not random, but gradual increases and decreases (Vander Zouwen 1983).

Coots changes from feeding on native macrophytes in earlier years to the abundant filamentous algae in recent years. Perhaps their flexible feeding habits and tolerance of human activity allowed them to be unaffected by habitat change through most of the study period. However, it may be significant that coot use declined from a peak in 1975 to the lowest use of the study period in 1979 and 1980, concurrent with a decline in all vegetation. Indeed, coot use has been correlated with vegetative abundance elsewhere (Duke and Chabrek 1976, Bellrose et al. 1979).

IMPLICATIONS

A small refuge, even near an urban area, can have diverse and abundant waterfowl use if habitat conditions are suitable. However, such areas are at high risk to habitat degradation and disturbance.

The decline in value of the Bay and even Lake Mendota, of which it is a part, as a fall concentration site probably has not significantly affected flyway waterfowl populations. However, the conditions on the Bay and Lake Mendota are not unique. Rapid urbanization, intensive agriculture, and increasing human activity in the shrinking water acreage are prevalent through much of the country in important waterfowl areas.

In Wisconsin, Lake Koshkonong vied with Chesapeake Bay for hunting diving ducks in the late 1800's (Hallock 1879). Water level fluctuations, turbidity, and rough-fish populations caused vegetative decline, and today relatively few divers use it (Jahn and Hunt 1964). The Winnebago-area lakes (Poygan, Winneconne, and Buttes des Mortes) were the most important diver concentration area in Wisconsin as late as the 1950's (Jahn and Hunt 1964). Habitat degradation was followed by much reduced diver use (A. Lynde, T. Hanson, W. Wheeler pers. commun.). Habitat degradation or human activity have also contributed to the decline in waterfowl use of Minnesota lakes (R. Jessen pers. commun.), the Illinois River Valley (Mills et al. 1966, Bellrose et al. 1979), Chesapeake Bay (Perry et al. 1981), Humboldt Bay, California (Henry 1980), and portions of the Mississippi River (C. Korschgen pers. commun.). There are doubtless many more waterfowl concentration areas of equal or lesser importance that have similarly been adversely affected.

In Wisconsin, wetland acreage has been reduced from 10 to 2.5 million acres since pristine times (Wheeler and March 1979). Loss of wetlands across the continent has been similarly extensive (Sanderson and Bellrose 1960). It is far easier to determine loss of wetland acreage than to determine the acreage that is present but no longer of value to waterfowl due to habitat degradation or human activity. The latter must be recognized in considering resources available to waterfowl. Many investigators have shown that selection of water areas for breeding, migration, and wintering depend on food supplies (e.g., Barstow 1957, Bergman 1973, White and James 1978, Bellrose et al. 1979, Joyner 1980, Hobaugh and Teer 1981).

The loss of wetlands together with the degradation and reduced value of others results in decreased resource availability for waterfowl in migration that may cause ducks to arrive on wintering grounds in poor condition (Frederickson and Drobney 1979). Concentration of waterfowl on remaining stopover areas, such as has occurred on the Mississippi River, may adversely affect waterfowl energy budgets (Frederickson and Drobney 1979) and provides increased potential for disease outbreaks (Friend 1975). As Weller (1975:106) pointed out, "Part time use of many areas in a vast network of habitats seems to be part of the ecological strategy of a continental waterfowl population. A reduction in number of areas available can only result in increased competition for food and space, and the eventual loss of a portion of the population." The stress that increased concentration and overflying has on waterfowl populations may be or may become significant.

One aim of waterfowl management is to improve or maintain the distribution and abundance of waterfowl for recreational purposes. The concentration of waterfowl on the remaining suitable habitats also affects consumptive and nonconsumptive uses by reducing distribution and availability.

Weller (1975) suggested that one of the ways waterfowl adapt from low breeding densities to high wintering densities is by feeding at lower trophic levels (animal to plant) where food is more abundant. As I pointed out earlier, vegetative decline has resulted in the change in food habits of some species from plant to animal food. What will be the effect of this change on these populations which have evolved as plant consumers, and what will be the effect of migrating and wintering waterfowl feeding at a higher trophic level?

Reduced water quality forces managers to rely on moist-soil plant production. It would be cheaper, more esthetically pleasing, and advantageous to more wildlife if many wetlands were maintained in their natural state. Moist-soil plants cannot be an adequate food substitute for wigeon, coot and many divers that rely on submergent vegetation.

The implications of Eurasian watermilfoil invasions to waterfowl are not clear. Invasion by this species in the Bay resulted in decreased use only by canvasback and redhead, but affected the spatial distribution of divers, dabblers, and coot on the Bay. Ryan (1972) suggested that a watermilfoil invasion was partially responsible for overwinter weight loss of redheads on Lake Seneca, New York. Eurasian watermilfoil received little use by waterfowl in Chesapeake Bay (Perry et al. 1981) but considerable use by some waterfowl in Back Bay, Virginia and Currtituck Sound, North Carolina (Florschutz 1972). This exotic plant has invaded and become dominant in many waters in the eastern United States (Nichols 1975) and in California and British Columbia (Carpenter 1979), but there is little documentation concerning its effects on waterfowl. More information on this subject would aid in evaluating the impact of Eurasian watermilfoil on the welfare of waterfowl.

The reclamation and subsequent high waterfowl use of Nielsen Marsh indicates a potential for waterfowl management through setting aside drained and cultivated wetland areas for reclamation, thus providing added food and space resources for waterfowl. Benson and Foley (1956) also found that the creation of small marshes in New York served as fall concentration points for locally-reared ducks and migrants. Publicizing the value of reclaimed wetlands might encourage private landowners to set aside such lands.

MANAGEMENT RECOMMENDATIONS

One of the 4 most important objectives of waterfowl conservation is habitat preservation and enhancement (Bellrose 1976). Acquisition of wetlands has been a primary goal of waterfowl managers, and rightly so, but more attention should be given to maintaining wetlands already preserved, lest they be degraded to the point of being of little value to waterfowl. Maintenance of natural wetlands may be more difficult, because this often necessitates the working together of many agencies as well as landowners.

Management for food not only includes wetland management but also watershed management, because vegetation and invertebrate abundance and diversity are adversely affected by pollution, eutrophication, siltation, and resultant turbidity. Steenis (1950) and Hobaugh and Teer (1981) suggested soil conservation practices such as terracing, restrictions on steep-slope farming, reforestation, farm-pond construction, and catch basins be used for controlling siltation to enhance water quality and aquatic vegetation. Some incentives through ASCS are available to landowners. Street-sweeping reduced substantially storm-sewer nutrient and particulate loadings in Madison, Wisconsin (Ahern 1976). Restrictions on application of fertilizers, salt, and herbicides should be considered. Effective waste-water treatment is a necessity if such water degrades wetlands. Within concentration sites, agents that resuspend sediments such as rough-fish and wind and wave action should be controlled whenever possible, particularly the former because they also uproot vegetation. Emergent vegetation reduces the effect of wind and waves. Priority should be given to sites that are most diverse and remain ice-free longest, because they supply the needs of the maximum number of waterfowl species.

Human activity is becoming increasingly important with increased shoreline development, fall fishing, and concentration of hunters on fewer wetlands. If ducks are to benefit, some areas must be protected from human disturbance. Each area should be evaluated separately. In a multi-use area, such as the Bay, human activity cannot easily be controlled. Areas important to waterfowl should be closed to boat traffic during peak migration periods. Where refuges are already established for protection from hunting, recreational boating and fishing should be prohibited as well. Protection from human disturbance is especially important on small areas similar to the Bay; in such areas shore activity should also be limited.

These recommendations are not necessarily new, but they need to be emphasized. These findings provide support for initiating conservation practices needed for the well being of the waterfowl resource.

ACKNOWLEDGEMENTS

I thank Robert A. McCabe for guiding me through this project. It was he who orchestrated the collection of data over most of the 33 years, and it was his vision that shaped the course of the analysis. I acknowledge the many graduate students who participated in the collection of data for this project. I thank J. Cary for help analyzing data. Funds were provided by the Max McGraw Wildlife Foundation and the Department of Wildlife Ecology, College of Agricultural and Life Sciences, University of Wisconsin-Madison. I thank the U.S. Fish and Wildlife Service for permission to use harvest, breeding population, and Upper Mississippi River Refuge waterfowl use data. R. Trost reviewed the manuscript.

LITERATURE CITED

Ahern, J. 1976. Impact and management of urban runoff. M.S. Thesis. Univ. Wis.-Madison. 207pp.

Anderson, H. G. 1959. Food habits of migratory ducks in Illinois. *Illinois Natural History Survey Bulletin* 27:289–344.

Andrews, J. D. 1946. The macroscopic invertebrate populations of the larger aquatic plants in Lake Mendota. Ph.D. Thesis. Univ. Wis.-Madison. 104pp.

Andrews, J. D., and A. D. Hasler. 1943. Fluctuations in the animal populations of the littoral zone in Lake Mendota. *Transactions of* the Wisconsin Academy of Science, Arts, and Letters 35:175–185.

Atlantic Flyway Council. 1972. *Techniques handbook of waterfowl habitat development and management.* 2nd Ed. Atlantic Flyway Council. Bolton, MA. 218pp.

Barstow, C. J. 1957. A comparative study of availability of waterfowl foods and waterfowl use on a series of clean and turbid farm ponds in north-central Oklahoma. *Proceedings Southeast Association Game and Fish Commission* 11:364–372.

Bartelt, G. A. 1977. Aspects of the population ecology of the American coot in Wisconsin. M.S. Thesis. Univ. Wis.-Madison. 38pp.

Bellrose, F. C. 1954. Value of waterfowl refuges in Illinois. *Journal of Wildlife Management* 18(2):160–169.

Bellrose, F. C. 1976. *Ducks, geese, and swans of North America.* Stackpole Books, Harrisburg, Pa. 544pp.

Bellrose, F. C., F. L. Paveglio, and D. W. Steffeck. 1979. Waterfowl populations and the changing environment of the Illinois River Valley. *Illinois Natural History Survey Bulletin* 32(1):1–54.

Benson, D. and D. Foley. 1956. Waterfowl use of small, man-made wildlife marshes in New York State. *New York Fish and Game Journal* 3(2):217–224.

Bergman, R. D. 1973. Use of southern boreal lakes by post-breeding canvasbacks and redheads. *Journal of Wildlife Management* 37:160–170.

Bortleson, G. E., and G. F. Lee. 1972. Recent sediment history of Lake Mendota, Wisconsin. *Environmental Science and Technology* 6:799–808.

Bunge, W. W., and R. A. Bryson. 1956. Ice on Wisconsin lakes. Report to the University of Wisconsin lake investigations committee. No. 13. 83pp.

Carpenter, S. R. 1979. The invasion and decline of *Myriophyllum spicatum* in an eutrophic Wisconsin lake. Pp. 11–32. *In* Aquatic Plants, Lake Management and Ecosystem Consequences of Lake Harvesting. Institute for Environmental Studies. Madison, Wis. 435pp.

Chabrek, R. H. 1979. Winter habitat of dabbling ducks—physical, chemical and biological aspects. *In* T. A. Bookhout, ed. Waterfowl and wetlands—an integrated review. 152pp.

Cornelius, S. E. 1977. Food and resource utilization by wintering redheads on lower Laguna Madre. *Journal of Wildlife Management* 41(3):374–385.

Cottam, C. 1939. Food habits of North American diving ducks. *USDA Technical Bulletin* 643. 140pp.

Cottam, C., and F. M. Uhler. 1937. Birds in relation to fishes. *Bureau Biological Survey, Wildlife Resource Management Leaflet* BS-83. 16pp.

Cowardin, L. M. 1969. Use of flooded timber by waterfowl at the Montezuma National Wildlife Refuge. *Journal of Wildlife management* 33(4):829–842.

Cronan, J. M. 1957. Food and feeding habits of the scaups in Connecticut waters. *Auk* 74(4):459–468.

Davis, G. J., and M. M. Brinson. 1980. Responses of submerged vascular plant communities to environmental change. *U.S. Fish and Wildlife Service Biological Service Program* FWS/OBS-79/33. 70pp.

Denniston, R. H. 1921. A survey of the larger aquatic plants in Lake Mendota. *Transactions of the Wisconsin Academy of Science, Arts, and Letters* 20:495–400.

Dillon, S. T. 1956. A nine-year study of fall waterfowl migration on University Bay, Madison, Wisconsin; Part I. *Transactions of the Wisconsin Academy of Science, Arts, and Letters* 45:31–57.

Dillon, S. T. 1956. A nine-year study of fall waterfowl migration on University Bay, Madison, Wisconsin; Part II. *Transactions of the Wisconsin Academy of Science, Arts, and Letters* 46:1–30.

Duke, R. W., and R. H. Chabrek. 1976. Waterfowl habitat in lakes of the Atchafalaya Basin, Louisiana. *Proceedings Southeast Association Game and Fish Commission* 29:501–512.

Erskine, A. J. 1972. Buffleheads. *Canadian Wildlife Service Monograph Series* 4. 240pp.

Figley, W. K., and L. W. VanDruff. 1982. The ecology of urban mallards. *Wildlife Monographs* No. 81. 40pp.

Florschutz, O. 1972. The Eurasian watermilfoil (*Myriophyllum spicatum*) as a waterfowl food. *Proceedings Southeast Association Game and Fish Commission* 26:189–194.

Frederickson, G. H., and R. D. Drobney. 1979. Habitat utilization by post-breeding waterfowl. Pp. 119–132. *In* T. A. Bookhout, (ed.) *Waterfowl and wetlands—an integrated review.* 152pp.

Friend, M. 1975. New dimensions in diseases affecting waterfowl. *Proceeding International Waterfowl Symposium* 1:155–162.

Hallock, C. 1879. *The sportsman's gazetteer and general guide.* 5th ed. Forest and Stream Publ. Co., New York. 908pp.

Hawkins, A. S. 1964. Mississippi Flyway. Pp. 185–207. *In* J. P. Linduska, (ed.) *Waterfowl Tomorrow.* U.S. Gov. Printing Office, Wash., D.C. 770pp.

Henry, W. G. 1980. Populations and behavior of black brant at Humboldt Bay, California. M.S. Thesis. 101pp.

Hobaugh, W. C., and J. G. Teer. 1981. Waterfowl use characteristics of flood-prevention lakes in north-central Texas. *Journal of Wildlife Management* 45(1):16–26.

Hochbaum, H. A. 1955. Travels and traditions of waterfowl. Univ. Minn. Press, Minneapolis, Minn. 301pp.

Jahn, L. R., R. C. Hopkins, and H. C. Jordahl. 1958. Protection for waterfowl in fall. *Wisconsin Conservation Bulletin* 23(9):13–17.

Jahn, L. R., and R. A. Hunt. 1964. Duck and coot ecology and management in Wisconsin. *Wisconsin Conservation Department Technical Bulletin* 33. 212pp.

Jonasson, P. M. 1969. Bottom fauna and eutrophication. Pp. 274–305. *In Proceedings International Symposium on Eutrophication*. Nat. Acad. of Sci. 661pp.

Joyner, D. E. 1980. Influence of invertebrates on pond selection by ducks in Ontario. *Journal of Wildlife Management* 44(3):700–705.

Kiel, W. H., A. S. Hawkins, and N. G. Perret. 1972. Waterfowl habitat trends in the aspen parklands of Manitoba. *Canadian Wildlife Service Report Series* 18:1–63.

Krecker, F. H. 1939. A comparative study of the animal populations of certain submerged aquatic plants. *Ecology* 20(4):553–562.

Krull, J. N. 1970. Aquatic plant-macroinvertebrate associations and waterfowl. *Journal of Wildlife Management* 34(4):707–718.

Lind, C. T. and G. Cottam. 1969. The submerged aquatics of University Bay: A study in eutrophication. *American Midland Naturalist* 81:353–369.

Low, J. B. and F. C. Bellrose. 1944. The seed and vegetative yield of waterfowl food plants in the Illinois River Valley. *Journal of Wildlife Management* 8(1):7–22.

Martin, E. M., and S. M. Carney. 1977. Population ecology of the mallard, IV. A review of duck hunting regulations, activity, and success, with special reference to the mallard. *U.S. Fish and Wildlife Services Resource Publication* 130. 137pp.

McGaha, Y. J. 1952. The limnological relations of insects to certain aquatic flowering plants. *Transactions American Microscopic Society* 71:355–381.

Mendall, H. L. 1958. The ring-necked duck of the northeast. *University of Maine Bulletin* 60. 317pp.

Mills, H. B., W. C. Starrett, and F. C. Bellrose. 1966. Man's effect on the fish and wildlife of the Illinois River. *Illinois Natural History Survey Biological Notes* 57. 24pp.

Morgan, N. C. 1970. Changes in the fauna and flora of a nutrient enriched lake. *Hydrobiologia* 35:545–553.

Moyle, J. B. 1961. Aquatic invertebrates as related to large water plants and waterfowl. *Minnesota Department of Conservation Investigative Report No.* 233. 24pp.

Munro, J. A. 1949. Studies of waterfowl in British Columbia. *Canadian Journal of Research* 27(5):289–307.

Nichols, S. A. 1975. Identification and management of Eurasian watermilfoil in Wisconsin. *Transactions of Wisconsin Academy of Science, Arts, and Letters* 63:166–128.

Olney, P. J. 1963. The autumn and winter feeding biology of certain sympatric ducks. *Transactions of the Congress of the International Union of Game Biologists* 6:309–320.

Paloumpis, A. A., and W. C. Starrett. 1960. An ecological study of benthic organisms in three Illinois river floodplain lakes. *American Midland Naturalist* 64(2):406–435.

Perry, M. C., R. E. Munro, and G. M. Haramis. 1981. Twenty-five year trends in diving duck populations in Chesapeake Bay. *Proceedings North American Wildlife Conference* 46:299–310.

Pirnie, M. D. 1940. Small area management for waterfowl. *Transactions North American Wildlife Conference* 5:387–391.

Rogers, J. P., and L. J. Korschgen. 1966. Foods of lesser scaups on breeding, migration, and wintering areas. *Journal of Wildlife Management* 30(2):258–264.

Ryan, R. A. 1972. Body weight and weight changes of wintering diving ducks. *Journal of Wildlife Management* 36(3):759–765.

Sanderson, G. C. and F. C. Bellrose. 1969. Wildlife habitat management of wetlands. *An. Acad. Brasil Cienc.* 41(supplement):153–204.

Schroeder, L. D. 1973. A literature review on the role of invertebrates in waterfowl management. *Colorado Division of Wildlife Special Report No.* 29. 13pp.

Smith, T. S. 1975. The Wisconsin duck harvest 1961–1970 as determined from the wing collection surveys. M.S. Thesis. Univ. Wis., Stevens Point. 351pp.

Steenis, J. H. 1950. Waterfowl habitat improvement on Reelfoot Lake. *Journal Tennessee Academy of Science* 15(1):56–64.

Sterrett, R. J. 1975. The geology and hydrogeology of University Bay, Madison, Wisconsin. M.S. thesis. Univ. Wis.-Madison. 162pp.

Stewart, R. E. 1962. Waterfowl populations in the upper Chesapeake Bay region. *U.S. Fish and Wildlife Service Special Scientific Report, Wildlife* 65. 208pp.

Stewart, R. E., A. D. Geis, and C. D. Evans. 1958. Distribution of populations and hunting kill of the canvasback. *Journal of Wildlife Management* 22:333–370.

Thompson, D. 1973. Feeding ecology of diving ducks on Keokuk Pool, Mississippi River. *Journal of Wildlife Management* 37(3):367–381.

Thornburg, D. D. 1973. Diving duck movements on Keokuk Pool, Mississippi River. *Journal of Wildlife Management* 37(3):387–389.

United States Fish and Wildlife Service. 1956–1976. Waterfowl Status Reports.

United States Fish and Wildlife Service. 1976–1981. Administrative Reports.

Vander Zouwen, W. J. 1982. Vegetational change in University Bay from 1966 to 1980. *Transactions Wisconsin Academy of Science, Arts, and Letters* 70:42–51.

Weller, M. W. 1975. Migratory waterfowl: a hemispheric perspective. *Publicaciones Biologicas, Instituto de Investigaciones científicas UANL* 1(8):89–130.

Wheeler, W. F., and J. R. March. 1979. Characteristics of scattered wetlands in relation to duck production in southeastern Wisconsin. *Wisconsin Technical Bulletin No.* 116. 61pp.

White, D. H., and D. James. 1978. Differential use of fresh water environments by wintering waterfowl of coastal Texas. *Wilson Bulletin* 90:99–111.

William J. Vander Zouwen
Bureau of Wildlife Management
Wisconsin DNR
Madison, WI 53716

Buffleheads (2nd place 1992 Wisconsin Duck Stamp competition) *by Frank Mittelstadt.*

Gray Jay *by Frank Mittelstadt.*

Forest Management and Birds in Northern Wisconsin

The habitat needs of key forest bird species are discussed in light of how forest management practices alter habitat. We focus on 5 groups: source/core species, isolation-sensitive species, edge-sensitive species, area-sensitive species, and species with special needs.

by Robert W. Howe, Stanley A. Temple and Michael J. Mossman

Northern Wisconsin contains vast acreages of publicly owned and managed forests, which provide breeding habitat for at least 170 bird species. These national, state, and county forests are important not only for their several rare and endangered species, but also for more common ones that find especially productive habitats there. To help assure that bird species do not lose out among the various, often conflicting goals of these public lands, it is essential to identify their critical habitat requirements and threats, and determine management strategies that will encourage viable long-term populations. Birds are among the best known animals in forests of northern Wisconsin and their status, distribution, and habitat associations have been described by Robbins (1991) and in this journal's series "Birding the Habitat Way" (e.g., Hoffman 1989, Hoffman and Mossman 1990). Nevertheless, considerable uncertainty prevails about the effects of forest management on many species, and birds have been prominent in debates about the ecological consequences of forest management (e.g., Kuhlman 1990). During September of 1992 the U.S. Forest Service convened a Scientific Roundtable of experts to consider recommendations for managing biological diversity in the two national forests (Nicolet and Chequamegon) of northern Wisconsin. This article elaborates the recommendations of a sub-group focusing on the impacts of forest management on native bird species. These recommendations pertain not only to National Forests, but to other public forests in northern Wisconsin as well. In addition to the authors, other participants in the sub-group were Michael Coffman and Peter Wagner; we gratefully acknowledge their contributions to the ideas presented here.

We report general information about the habitat needs of key species; based on this information, we speculate how forest management practices might best help sustain existing populations of native species. Following the approach of Taylor (1990), we begin by recognizing categories of bird species that are associated with specific threats or management objectives. For each category, we identify representative species, future information needs, and recommendations aimed at maintaining viable populations in northern Wisconsin.

SOURCE/CORE SPECIES

Perhaps the most important group of species for consideration by Forest managers includes species whose geographic range is centered in the Upper Great Lakes Region. Northern Wisconsin is inhabited by no endemic bird species, but certain species appear to be more abundant, widespread or productive here than in most or other regions. We call these birds source/core species (Table 1) because a surplus of young produced in northern Wisconsin populations might be vitally important for maintaining global populations.

Ovenbird and Hermit Thrush are particularly good examples. Ovenbirds are known to be sensitive to habitat fragmentation and other forest modifications, but this species is thriving in northern Wisconsin (Hoffman and Mossman 1990, Howe et al. 1993). Quite possibly, emigrants from northern Wisconsin and similar areas might be critical for sustaining populations on a regional or continental scale (Temple and Cary 1987). Mourning Warbler, Golden-winged Warbler,

Nashville Warbler, and Chestnut-sided Warbler likewise appear to be unusually successful in northern Wisconsin. Other source/core species like Scarlet Tanager, Black-and-white Warbler, and Purple Finch are not abundant in northern Wisconsin, yet populations in the region are very likely as large and productive as populations anywhere else (Robbins et al. 1986).

Monitoring of source/core species should measure demographic success as well as abundance. Effective habitat protection should recognize "production areas" where conditions are ideal for survival and reproduction. Identification of these areas will not be easy, but it may be the most significant conservation effort that could be implemented.

ISOLATION-SENSITIVE SPECIES

Due to their rarity and low vagility, several isolation-sensitive species in northern Wisconsin are vulnerable to effects of small population size. Spruce Grouse, Sharp-tailed Grouse, Gray Jay, and Boreal Chickadee are usually non-migratory and are restricted to localized areas of special habitat (conifer swamp and jack pine forest for the Spruce Grouse, open barrens for the sharp-tail, conifer and mixed swamp for the jay, and black spruce bog for the chickadee). Inbreeding, loss of genetic variation, and local extinction are potential problems for these populations because immigration from other areas may not counteract genetic drift and demographic catastrophes. Fritz (1979) showed that recolonizations of vacated Spruce Grouse territories in New Hampshire require many years if recolonization occurs at all. Northern Wisconsin populations of isolation-sensitive species are likewise small and poorly connected with other local populations.

Probably the most straightforward recommendation for this group of species is to identify where local populations occur. Once identified, these populations need to be monitored regularly to signal local declines or increases. In the long term, consideration of habitat corridors and translocations are more appropriate for these species than for others. The general mobility of birds and seasonal shifts in the distribution of many species dictate that few birds in northeastern Wisconsin can be considered isolation-sensitive. Other appropriate actions may include tighter hunting regulations for grouse, and management to increase habitat size and suitability. Species of other taxonomic groups (e.g., small mammals, soil invertebrates, native herbaceous plants, etc.) are much more likely to fit this category and need to be given the same considerations described above for isolation-sensitive birds (Table 1).

EDGE-SENSITIVE SPECIES

Evidence for negative impacts of forest edges has accumulated from many areas. Increased levels of predation (Gates and Gysel 1979), brood parasitism (Brittingham and Temple 1983), and competition (Ambuel and Temple 1983), appear to harm certain species more than others (Temple and Cary 1987). Ground-foraging birds (e.g., Wood Thrush, Hermit Thrush, Winter Wren) and open-nesting songbirds (e.g., warblers, vireos) are particularly vulnerable. Edge effects have not been well studied in northern Wis-

consin forests, but the species involved with these phenomena are present and presumably can affect the ecological environment to some degree. We have documented brood parasitism of nests of 14 species.

Schneider (1992) recorded little difference in the abundance of birds along edges vs. interior of hardwood forests of the Nicolet National Forest. Howe et al. (1992), on the other hand, documented higher abundances of American Crow and American Robin along roadside sites compared with forest interior sites of the Nicolet National Forest Bird Survey. Clearly, additional studies are needed to assess the effects of forest edges on birds in northern Wisconsin. Different types of edges (logging trails, primary roads, clear cuts, wildlife openings, etc.) probably have different degrees of impact on forest birds. Major impacts do not seem to be physical or even physiographical, insofar as few birds have been shown to avoid forest edges in northern Wisconsin. The most serious edge effects in northern Wisconsin appear to be mediated through species interactions. Michael Grimm (personal communication) found that Spruce Grouse in the Nicolet National Forest occur primarily or exclusively in remote wilderness. In this case, edge effects are probably mediated through hunting; in other cases, species interactions (predation, competition, etc.) can have the same consequence. House Wrens affect Winter Wrens negatively as forests become fragmented (Wolf and Howe 1991). Great Horned Owls and Red-tailed Hawks invade areas where forest openings are extensive. Their effects on forest species like Barred Owls, Red-shouldered

Table 1. Management categories of northern Wisconsin birds with representative examples. Descriptions of categories are provided in text.

Species	Source/Core Species	Isolation-sensitive Species	Edge-sensitive Species	Area-sensitive Species	Special Needs Species
Hooded Merganser	X				
American Woodcock	X				
Sharp-shinned Hawk	X				
Broad-winged Hawk	X				
Black-billed Cuckoo	X				
Barred Owl	X				
Northern Saw-whet Owl	X				
Yellow-bellied Sapsucker	X				
Least Flycatcher	X				
Brown Creeper	X				
Winter Wren	X				
Veery	X				
Hermit Thrush	X				
Golden-winged Warbler	X				
Nashville Warbler	X				
Black-and-white Warbler	X				
Blackburnian Warbler	X				
Chestnut-sided Warbler	X				
Black-throated Green Warbler	X				
Mourning Warbler	X				
Ovenbird	X				
Rose-breasted Grosbeak	X				
Scarlet Tanager	X				
Purple Finch	X				
Spruce Grouse		X			
Sharp-tailed Grouse		X			
Boreal Chickadee		X			
Gray Jay		X			
Spruce Grouse			X		
Barred Owl			X		
Least Flycatcher			X		
Ruby-crowned Kinglet			X		
Swainson's Thrush			X		
Wood Thrush			X		
Solitary Vireo			X		
Red-eyed Vireo			X		
Black-throated Blue Warbler			X		
Black-throated Green Warbler			X		
Blackburnian Warbler			X		
Black-and-white Warbler			X		
Canada Warbler			X		
Scarlet Tanager			X		
Red-shouldered Hawk				X	
Northern Goshawk				X	
Sharp-tailed Grouse				X	
Pileated Woodpecker				X	
Palm Warbler				X	
Lincoln's Sparrow				X	
LeConte's Sparrow				X	

(continued)

Table 1. *Continued*

Species	Source/Core Species	Isolation-sensitive Species	Edge-sensitive Species	Area-sensitive Species	Special Needs Species
Hooded Merganser (nest cavities)					X
Bald Eagle (nest trees)					X
Black-backed Woodpecker (dead trees)					X
Pileated Woodpecker (large trees)					X
Red-breasted Nuthatch (nest cavities)					X
Brown Creeper (nest cavities)					X
Veery (understory vegetation)					X
Cedar Waxwing (fruiting trees or shrubs)					X
Northern Parula (*Usnea* lichens)					X
Black-throated Blue Warbler (dense understory)					X
Blackburnian Warbler (large conifers w/hardwoods)					X
Pine Warbler (mature or extensive conifers)					X
Northern Waterthrush (wooded watercourses)					X
White-winged Crossbill (seed-producing conifers)					X
Evening Grosbeak (seed/fruit producing trees)					X

Hawks, and prey species are not well documented, but absence of the latter species and abundance of the other two in partially deforested areas of Wisconsin implies that Great Horned Owls and Red-tailed Hawks influence other forest raptors significantly.

Even though edge effects have not been clearly documented in northern forests, a conservative management strategy for edge sensitive species (Table 1) calls for maintenance of areas where edge effects are minimized. How large should these areas be? A 20-ha (≈ 50 acre) rectangular block of forest contains only about 6 ha of "interior" habitat, assuming an edge effect of 100 m; a 200-ha block contains less than 150 ha, while a 2000-ha block

contains a maximum of 1850 ha of interior habitat (less if the boundary is non-circular). Management areas of hundreds or thousands of hectares obviously are needed to ensure that edge effects do not dominate the forest's ecology. Unfortunately, few if any unfragmented areas exist to provide a standard for comparison.

AREA-SENSITIVE SPECIES

Birds with large home ranges require extensive areas of appropriate habitat merely to satisfy their daily resource needs. In addition, species that nest or display colonially may also require large areas to maintain critical population sizes. Sharp-tailed Grouse are perhaps the clearest example of an area sensitive species in northern Wisconsin (Temple 1992). Local populations of this species need thousands of hectares of open habitat for long term survival. Forest species with low densities likewise require large habitat areas to sustain viable local populations. Red-shouldered Hawk, Pileated Woodpecker, and possibly many locally uncommon songbirds (e.g., Black-and-white Warbler) fit this category. Again, management for such species requires a geographically broad management perspective.

Area sensitivity in northern Wisconsin most obviously applies to species of non-forested habitats, which are naturally limited in extent. Bogs, for example, range in size from less than an acre to several square miles; bird species like Ruby-crowned Kinglet, Palm Warbler, Gray Jay, and perhaps other species are limited to the largest of these sites. Likewise, birds of sedge meadows like Sharp-tailed Sparrow, LeConte's Sparrow, Yellow Rail, and possibly Wilson's Phalarope are restricted to large habitat blocks (Mossman and Sample 1990). As barrens communities have been fragmented and shrunken by forest succession, some species have become limited to the very few remaining, large, managed tracts, for example Upland Sandpiper, Sharp-tailed Grouse, and Northern Harrier. Management of these habitats must begin with identification and protection of the largest representative areas. In the case of transient habitats like forest windthrows, burns, and meadows associated with beaver impoundments, long range planning is needed to identify areas where natural or simulated regeneration can be replicated.

SPECIES WITH SPECIAL NEEDS

All breeding bird species have particular requirements for factors such as habitat structure and composition, food resources, and nest sites. In northern Wisconsin forests, some species' requirements are fairly restrictive and/or easily identifiable. We have selected a few of these to illustrate specific habitat features that should be provided by forest management.

Cavity-nesting birds usually require dead or dying trees for excavation of nest sites. These special needs are addressed by forest management guidelines that call for retention of a prescribed density of snags or cavity trees. Are these policies successful? Our studies show that forest cavity nesters are widespread (but generally not abundant) in northern Wisconsin. Many of today's cavity nesting birds appear to be surviving well in managed forest. Unfortunately, we have little if any baseline date to provide an historical context. Black-backed Woodpecker, unlike the others, is very localized and rare in northern Wisconsin. If today's populations of this species are to survive, dead trees and blowdowns must be maintained in open habitats, fire-managed woodlands or swamplands.

Because cavity nesters are vulnerable to the effects of forest management, it is important to monitor their populations. Existing steps to provide or maintain cavity trees appear to be having a positive effect, but again evidence is largely anecdotal. Observations by wildlife biologists show that construction of artificial nest boxes has benefitted Wood Ducks, Hooded Mergansers, Eastern Bluebirds, Tree Swallows, and probably several other species. Forest managers should monitor designated wildlife trees or den trees after timber sales to determine whether standard management prescriptions are adequate.

Many other bird species have special needs; some of these needs have long been recognized and, in a few cases, these needs already are being addressed by Forest Service policies. Bald Eagles and Ospreys, for example, require large trees to support their nests; retention of large nest trees and (in the case of ospreys) construction of artificial nesting platforms is standard practice in public forests of northern Wisconsin. Other species have more subtle habitat requirements. Northern Parulas require (or at least favor) *Usnea* lichens for nesting material. Ruby-throated Hummingbirds require nectar-producing flowers. Black-throated Blue Warblers require patches of dense understory with shrubs like elderberry. Northern Waterthrushes require forested stream edges or wet woodland and tree tip-ups for nesting.

The special needs of these and other species were provided adequately in the pre-settlement forests of northern Wisconsin. Today, the landscape has changed, and some of the important habitat features have been eliminated locally or greatly reduced throughout the region. Surprisingly, no bird species in northern Wisconsin appear to be strictly dependent on old-growth forest, suggesting that careful forest management can promote the long-term persistence of most native bird species in this region.

Future management aimed at special habitat features can follow two alternative approaches: 1) protect large enough areas to ensure that special habitat needs are provided by natural processes and disturbance regimes; or 2) document the natural history and ecology of all species in order to identify measures that can mitigate the effects of timber harvest or other human-related disturbances. In the long term, the second of these alternatives might be the most expensive, and some combination of the two approaches is advisable.

DISCUSSION

The choice of 25 birds as management indicator species in the Nicolet National Forest and 12 as management indicator species in the Chequamegon National Forest reflects the belief that the health of bird populations parallels the health of many other species. Although birds are probably better known than any non-game animals, birds are not necessarily the best representatives of biological diversity. Birds are highly mobile and can take advantage of local opportunities or they can avoid locally poor conditions. Presumably this mobility is responsible, at least in part, for the complicated habitat relationships of birds in northern Wisconsin (Howe et al. 1992). Events in the non-breeding grounds can further obfuscate population trends for migrants.

Of course, birds are of considerable interest in their own right. Primary cavity-nesters (woodpeckers) can justifiably be considered keystone species (Gilbert 1980) whose effects on other species (e.g., forest trees and occupants of abandoned cavities) are highly significant. Frugivores such as Rose-breasted Grosbeaks, Blue Jays, and thrushes are important dispersers of seeds during and probably before fall migration. Insectivores and raptors undoubtedly have occasional (or possibly continuous) impacts on prey populations, some of which are pests.

Birds also are important as a source of recreation. More than 60 million Americans are active in feeding wild birds, and each year nearly 30 million people in the U.S. aged 16 years or older travel from their homes with the intention of interacting with wildlife; songbirds represent the most common form of wildlife observed by these people (Harrington 1991).

Most bird species in northern Wisconsin (as with nearly every community of organisms) are relatively uncommon. Of 108–120 species recorded during the annual Nicolet National Forest Bird Survey between 1988 and 1992, for example, approximately 70–80% were recorded at fewer than 10% of the 150+ annual sampling points (Howe et al. 1992). Approximately 15–25% of these species were recorded at only 1 site. Clearly, many species are vulnerable to local and large scale habitat modification, if only because their populations are quite small.

Conservation of bird populations in northern Wisconsin's national forests is not likely to be successful unless accurate inventory, research and monitoring data are available. Up-to-date information enables Forest Service authorities to practice "adaptive management," whereby changes in policies can be implemented when monitoring data document a serious decline in desirable species. Of course, averting such declines in the first place is a more effective means of long term conservation. This can be accomplished by directing management actions at vulnerable species or by protecting large enough areas where natural ecological processes obviate specific management

actions. The first of these options will require more detailed field research on the ecology and status of target species; the latter will require a reconsideration of areas where logging or other human disturbances are minimized.

LITERATURE CITED

Ambuel, B. and S.A. Temple. 1983. Area dependent changes in bird communities of southern Wisconsin forests. *Ecology* 64:1057–1068.

Brittingham, M.C. and S.A. Temple. 1983. Have cowbirds caused forest songbirds decline? *Bioscience* 33:31–35.

Fritz, R.S. 1979. Consequences of insular population structure: distribution and extinction of Spruce Grouse populations. *Oecologia* 42:57–65.

Gates, J.E. and L.W. Gysel. 1978. Avian nest dispersion and fledgling success in field-forest ecotones. *Ecology* 59:871–883.

Gilbert, L.E. 1980. Food web organization and conservation of neotropical diversity. Pp. 11–34. *In* M.E. Soule and B.A. Wilcox (eds.), *Conservation Biology*, Sinauer Assoc., Sunderland, MA.

Harrington, W. 1991. Wildlife: severe decline and partial recovery. Pp. 205- 248. *In* K.D. Frederick and R.A. Sedjo, (eds.), *Americas Renewable Resources: Historical Trends and Current Challenges*, Resources for the Future, Inc., Washington, DC.

Hoffman, R.M. 1989. Birds of Wisconsin northern mesic forests. *Passenger Pigeon* 51:99–110.

Hoffman, R.M. and M.J. Mossman. 1990. Birds of northern Wisconsin pine forests. *Passenger Pigeon* 52:339–355.

Howe, R.W., A.T. Wolf, and T. Rinaldi. 1993. Monitoring birds in a regional landscape: lessons from the Nicolet National Forest Bird Survey. *In* C.J. Ralph, J. Sauer, J. and S. Droege, (eds.), *Monitoring Bird Populations Using Stationary Point Counts*. U.S. Forest Service Research Publication, Southwest Forest Experiment Station, Arcata, CA. *in press.*

Kuhlmann, W. 1990. A biological attack on timber primacy. *Forest Watch* 11:15–21.

Mossman, M.J. and D.W. Sample. 1990. Birds of Wisconsin sedge meadows. *Passenger Pigeon* 52:38–55.

Mossman, M.J., E.E. Epstein, and R.M. Hoffman. 1991. Birds of Wisconsin pine and oak barrens. *Passenger Pigeon* 53:137–163.

Robbins, C.S., D. Bystrak, and P.H. Geissler. 1986. *The Breeding Bird Survey: Its First Fifteen*

Years, 1965–1979. U.S.D.I. Fish and Wildlife Service Resource Publication 157, Washington, D.C.

Robbins, S.D., Jr. 1991. *Wisconsin Birdlife: Population and Distribution, Past and Present.* Univ. Wis. Press, Madison. 702pp.

Schneider, T.M. 1992. *Effects of logging roads on forest birds in the Nicolet National Forest.* M.S. Thesis, University of Wisconsin-Green Bay, Green Bay, WI.

Taylor, R.L. 1990. Avian indicators in the Chequamegon National Forest. *Passenger Pigeon* 52:225–231.

Temple, S.A. and J.R. Cary. 1988. Modeling the dynamics of forest-interior bird populations in a fragmented landscape. *Conservation Biology* 2:341–347.

Temple, S.A. 1992. Population viability analysis of a sharp-tailed grouse metapopulation in Wisconsin. In D.R. McCullough (ed.). *Wildlife 2000: Populations.* Elsevier Science, London.

Wolf, A.T. and R.W. Howe. 1991. The Winter Wren in Wisconsin. *Passenger Pigeon* 52:103–112.

Robert W. Howe
Department of Natural and
   Applied Sciences
University of Wisconsin-Green Bay
Green Bay, WI 54311–7001
Stanley A. Temple
Department of Wildlife Ecology
University of Wisconsin
Madison, WI 53706
Michael J. Mossman
Bureau of Research
Wisconsin Department of Natural
   Resources
Madison, WI 53716

Yellow-headed Blackbird *by Frank Mittelstadt.*

"Morning Preen" (Great Egret) *by Frank Mittelstadt.*

The Spring Season: 1992

by Allen K. Shea

In a state as large and geographically diverse as Wisconsin, it is difficult at best to characterize three months of weather in a few short paragraphs. As was done for last spring's field notes, perhaps the best way to try to capsulize the weather is to review what you, the observers, recorded about spring 1992's weather:

Southern (Milwaukee and Jefferson Counties)—"The month came in like the proverbial lamb with a high temperature of 64 degrees on March 1 and strong southwest winds. This changed rapidly as the remainder of March was dominated by below normal temperatures. Wintery weather in the form of ice and snow appeared on March 10 and heavy snow fell on March 22." April was "very cloudy, cool and rainy. Cloudy roughly 70% of the time. Total amount of rain was only 3.55″, but it rained on 16 separate days, including snow flurries April 1. Sixteen days were in the 40's or less (one in the 30's)." May was "dry [with] only 1.3″ (normal is 3.34″). Month ran hot and cool as various weather systems moved through." From May 1 to May 4, the wind went from south to northwest and temperature dropped from 82 to 52 degrees. From May 16 to May 18, the wind went from southwest to the northwest and temperatures from 86 to 71 degrees. From May 22 to May 24, the wind went from south to north and temperatures fell from 88 to 46 degrees.

Central (Portage County)—"March 1's 63 degrees was not a note of things to come. Except for the 50 degrees on March 24 and 25, the entire month was chilly, with continual mid-30's highs, falling back to winter cold from the 9th to the 15th with single digits for lows and highs in the 20's. Measurable precipitation was 1.25″ rain on the 7th-9th, 3.0″ of snow on the 13th, 5.0″ of snow on the 21st. April alternated 3–4 day periods of 50–60 degrees with 4–5 day periods of 30's; only reached 70 on the 30th. April 1's and 3's flurries and squalls didn't amount to much, nor did rainfall of 1.05″ for the month. The sun was absent from the 13th–26th. May's unremarkable weather was generally cool and pleasant, with unusually low humidity. 93% of the month's rainfall of 4.5″ fell on the 16th and 22nd. Frost occurred on the 24th. Looking kind of droughty at months end."

North (Douglas County)—"The first three weeks [of May] were normal, but the last week was cold at night. May 24th—snow flurries!, low 33 and cloudy; May 25th—low 28 degrees with a heavy frost; May 26th—low 22 degrees, heavy frost killed oak and ash leaves."

THE MIGRATION AT A GLANCE

Numerous observers recorded their impressions of the migration; some in great detail. These notes provide valuable insight into migration each spring and serve to illustrate that weather patterns can dramatically influence the shape of migration, real or perceived, across Wisconsin. Some excerpts:

"The spring season started out very well with an excellent waterfowl migration in early March . . . I have kept track of arrival dates for 20+ years in this area [Dane County]; this spring I had new early dates for 15 species of waterbirds . . . The mild weather in March and early April also made the landbird migration start out well . . . in fact, in comparison to last year's dismal migration, I would rate it as excellent." (Dane County)

"Best warbler migration in several years. Not very many individuals of each species but good total numbers of species each day." (Dane County)

"Gray-cheeked Thrushes, Swainson's Thrushes and Veerys staged the best migration in years. 12 Philadelphia Vireos were seen this spring [as compared to the] 18 year average of 2. Orange-crowned Warblers, Yellow-rumped Warblers and Palm Warblers were late in migrating. Very poor

White-crowned Sparrow migration [with] only 3 birds seen. Rails arrive very late with numbers in mid–May." (Southern Wisconsin)

"Migration was unremarkable throughout the period. Puddle duck numbers fell to zero, compared with the usual very few. Divers were about one-half usual concentrations, and had largely passed through by mid–April. An encounter with a diurnal raptor was a cause for celebration. April's persistent overcast (20 days) may have played a role, but May was almost as poor. Another year of few migrant thrushes and vireos leads me to conclude that this is the current norm for central Wisconsin. Sparrow arrival was about ten days late and with the normal departure dates, their migration was quite short." (Portage County)

"I think because of the nice weather we had in May, a lot of migrants flew over us and didn't stop. I found most warbler species that I get in spring . . . This was another good spring for sparrows." (Marathon County)

"Lots of ducks. It seems that they arrived then got stranded when northern lakes were still frozen . . . It was difficult to find warblers until well into May. Birds that should have been well represented by May 5 weren't seen for a week or so later. By May 15, everything seemed to be back on schedule. Shorebirds were spotty. Good areas had few birds." (Polk County)

"The migration season . . . this year would be classed as relatively poor . . . My suspicion is that many birds just over flew and continued to their breeding grounds. Did not have hundreds of yellow-rumps or no major waves of warblers. What we did have was sparce and we had to work for. Other than that, it has been okay species wise, with everything present, but with some lateness." (Oconto County)

Not surprisingly, observer's perspectives on the 1992 spring migration depended on where you were in the state and perhaps, even on what days you were out. Notwithstanding the variety of experiences evidenced above, in composite the spring was characterized by early arrival dates for a wide variety of species including new record early arrival dates for one gull, two shorebird and one warbler species; and arrival dates which tie the existing record arrival date for one flycatcher, and two additional warbler species.

Following are summaries of the migration of selected groups of species:

Waterfowl—A mild February resulted in water opening up early in the southern two-thirds of the state. Most southern Wisconsin birders acclaimed the early arrival dates and high numbers of almost all species. In fact, in the southern tier of counties, 'spring' had arrived prior to the beginning of the period for many species (see the species accounts).

Herons—As could be expected by the mild winter, over-wintering great blue herons were widespread. The remainder of the news was mixed: American Bitterns and Least Bitterns continue to have widespread reports across much of the state suggesting these species may have stable populations in protected wetlands. Yellow-crowned Night-herons continue to be scarce in the state and Black-crowned Night-herons and Great Egrets were rare away from the Horicon area.

Raptors—The mild winter resulted in widespread over-wintering of Sharp-shinned Hawk, Cooper's Hawk, and Northern Harrier. Red-shouldered Hawks were also reported at the beginning of the period in above average numbers. Goshawks were widespread both at the beginning and end of the period. Is this species following the 'wing beats' of the Cooper's Hawk and expanding its range in Wisconsin?

Rails—Records at new locations this spring again suggest we have much to learn about the migratory and breeding distribution of the Yellow Rails and King Rails.

Shorebirds—Judging from the abundance of records, spring 1992's shorebird migration appeared to be the best in several years. Whether this was induced by weather patterns, available habitat, observer acumen or a combination of all three is unknown, but the migration for most species was prolonged and widespread. This assessment is qualified by the supposition that there were a few hot spots scattered about the state which received widespread coverage. Lesser Golden Plovers and Black-bellied Plovers, both godwits and whimbrels made especially good showings.

Gulls—As with the other water-related birds, gulls were wide-spread across the southern one-half of the state at the beginning of the period. As per normal in the past few springs, a wide variety of rarities were observed. Of note were the continued increase in sightings of Greater Black-backed Gulls, a widespread and prolonged migration of Franklin's Gulls through the state, and rare inland sightings of Laughing Gulls and Little Gulls.

Warblers—Many observers around the state agreed on two aspects of the warbler migration this year: (1) species variety was excellent but numbers of individual species was low; and (2) peak movements occurred on the following dates: May 2–3, May 10–12, and May 16–17. May 17 was perhaps the peak movement of passerines into the state.

Flycatchers and Thrushes—A Dr. Jekyll and Mr. Hyde situation with some southern observers acclaiming it the best thrush and flycatcher migration in years and some northern observers descrying the paucity of these species. Apparently, weather patterns favored 'fallouts' of these species in southern Wisconsin which subsequently overflew the northern portions of the state.

Sparrows—Widely described as being late, the sparrow migration was notable by the dearth of White-crowned Sparrows statewide, the above average abundance of Grasshopper Sparrows, and the widespread distribution of both Henslow's Sparrows and LeConte's Sparrows.

POTPOURRI

Eighty-six observers submitted 138 separate county field report forms. The number of observers, while quite a bit below 1985's record of 109, was still above the sixteen-year average of 78. A remarkable 70 of 72 counties received coverage of some extent, a record for the spring season and well above the sixteen-year average of 63.

The counties receiving the most extensive coverage were as follows: Dodge with 16 separate reports; Dane and Milwaukee with 12 reports each;

Columbia and Manitowoc with 11 reports each; Bayfield, Ozaukee, Rock and Sheboygan with 8 reports each; Sauk and Waukesha with 6 reports each; and Ashland, Brown, Burnett, Green Lake, Jefferson, and Trempealeau with 5 reports each. The only two counties not receiving any coverage were Florence and Rusk.

A total of 307 species were reported during the period, 9 more than the sixteen year-average of 298, but 2 less than last year. Notable rare birds were: Snowy Egret, Little Blue Heron, Ross' Goose, Cinnamon Teal, Eurasian Widgeon, Swallow-tailed Kite, Gyrfalcon, Snowy Plover, Piping Plover, Laughing Gull, Thayer's Gull, Iceland Gull, Lesser Black-backed Gull, Great Black-backed Gull, Northern Hawk-owl, Great Gray Owl, Vermillion Flycatcher, Black-billed Magpie, Yellow-throated Warbler, and Western Tanager.

MISCELLANY

Abbreviations used in the following species accounts are: BOP = Beginning of the Period, EOP = End of the Period, TTP = Throughout the Period. Once again, I wish to extend a special thanks to Suzan Shea for her patience and moral support in preparing this report.

REPORTS (MARCH 1–MAY 31, 1992)

Red-throated Loon.—Reported as follows: Manitowoc County, March 28–April 23 (multiple observers); Sheboygan County, April 3–25 (multiple observers); Ozaukee County, April 12–17 (B. Domagalski and D. Gustafson); and Douglas County, May 2 (R. Johnson). On April 7, 13 birds were sighted in Manitowoc County (M. Korducki).

Common Loon.—First reported on March

10 in Dane and Sauk Counties (K. Burcar). On April 17, 35 birds were sighted in Chippewa County (J. Polk). A bird observed in Buffalo County on May 28 (F. Lesher) was late.

Pied-billed Grebe.—First reported in Dane County, March 2 (S. Robbins). On April 17, 96 birds were sighted in Dane County (K. Burcar).

Horned Grebe.—First reported in Marathon County, March 6 (D. Belter). On April 26, 65+ birds were sighted in Marathon County (D. Belter).

Red-necked Grebe.—First reported in Dane County, March 18 (K. Burcar). Also reported during the period in Ashland, Burnett, Chippewa, Dunn, Eau Claire, Green Lake, Marathon, Washington, and Winnebago Counties. On April 18, 36 birds were sighted in Douglas County (R. Johnson).

Eared Grebe.—Reported as follows: Manitowoc County, April 13–20 (multiple observers); Douglas County, April 22–25 (R. Johnson); Columbia County, May 17 (S. Robbins); and Dunn County, May 20–30 (M. Peterson and J. Polk)).

Western Grebe.—The only report for this species was of one bird May 9 in Burnett County (J. Hoefler).

American White Pelican.—A perhaps unprecedented number of Am. White Pelicans migrated through Wisconsin this spring. Reported as follows: Dane County, April 11, 2 birds (A Holzheuter); Green Lake County, April 16–27, 3 birds (T. Schultz); Southern Lake Michigan lakeshore, April 19, 35+ birds (fide J. Idzikowski); Douglas County, May 1–31, 3 birds (multiple observers); Grant County, May 3, 11 birds (K. Burcar and A. & S. Shea); Dunn County, May 6–8, 33 birds (J. Polk); Chippewa County, May 17, 10 birds (J. Polk); Ashland County, May 19–20, 4 birds (D. Verch); and Burnett County, May 29, 1 bird (M. Korducki and D. Tessen).

Double-crested Cormorant.—A bird in Winnebago County on March 2 was observed to have over wintered. Migrants were first reported in Dodge County, March 29 (K. Burcar & B. Domagalski). On April 22, 150+ birds were sighted in Douglas County (S. LaValley).

American Bittern.—First reported in Green County, April 7 (K. Burcar). On May 28, 18 birds were sighted in Burnett County (D. Tessen). Also reported in 26 other counties during the period.

Least Bittern.—First reported in Milwaukee County, May 1 (S. Diehl). Also reported during the period in Burnett, Columbia, Fond du Lac, Green Lake, Manitowoc, Marathon, Oconto, Taylor, Waukesha, and Winnebago Counties.

Great Blue Heron.—Present at the beginning of the period in Dodge, Fond du Lac, Monroe, Pierce, Sheboygan, and Trempealeau Counties.

Great Egret.—First reported in Dodge County, March 31 (K. Burcar).

Snowy Egret.—Reported as follows: Dodge County, April 23–25, 2 birds (multiple observers); Washington County, April 23 (M. Peterson); Milwaukee County, May 11 (B. Boldt); Calumet County, May 12 (C. Rudy); and Price County, May 31 (K. Merkel).

Little Blue Heron.—Reported as follows: Manitowoc County, April 18 (S. Baughman & C. Sontag); Washington County, April 25 (K. Burcar); and Dodge County, April 27–May 4 (B. Boldt).

Cattle Egret.—A good showing for this species this spring, with several records from outside this species normal range. Reported as follows: Monroe County, April 16–May 13 (D. Kuecherer); Dane County, April 23 (K. Burcar); Milwaukee County, May 2 (S. Diehl & M. Korducki); Grant County, May 3 (A. & S. Shea); Dane County, May 13 (E. Hansen); LaCrosse County, May 17 (J. Dankert); Sheboygan County, May 17 (Jeff Baumann & T. Schultz); Brown County, May 18 (M. Peterson); St. Croix County, May 19–23 (R. Hoffman & D. Lauten); Ashland County, May 20 (D. Verch) and Marathon County, May 24 (fide D. Belter).

Green-backed Heron.—First reported in Dane County, April 21 (K. Burcar).

Black-crowned Night-Heron.—First reported in Winnebago County, March 31 (D. Nussbaum).

Yellow-crowned Night-Heron.—Reported as follows: Outagamie County, April 20–25 (J. Anderson & S. Petznick); Outagamie County, April 25 (D. Nussbaum); Dane County, May 13–17 (R. Hoffman & A. Shea); and Buffalo County, May 26–27 (A. & S. Shea).

Tundra Swan.—First reported in Dane County, March 4 (E. Hansen). On April 8, 1,250 birds were sighted in Marathon County (D. Belter).

Trumpeter Swan.—Reported as follows: Polk County, TTP (J. Hudick); Trempealeau County, March 4–22 (J. Dankert & J. Hudick); Marathon County, March 21–May 6 (D. Belter); Green Lake County, May 22–23 (T. Schultz) and Burnett County, May 24–27 (M. Peterson and A. & S. Shea).

Mute Swan.—Present at the beginning of the period in Ashland, Bayfield, Dane, Douglas, Milwaukee, and Portage Counties. On May 4, 30 birds were sighted in Waukesha County (S. Diehl).

Greater White-fronted Goose.—Reported as follows: Jefferson County, March 1 (M. Korducki); Columbia County, March 7 (M. Peterson); Trempealeau County, March 7 (J. Dankert); Dane County, March 28 (K. Burcar); Dodge County, March 29 (K. Burcar & B. Domagalski); Dunn County, April 7 (J. Polk); and LaCrosse County, April 25 (J. Dankert). On March 14, 15 birds were sighted in Columbia County (D. Tessen).

Snow Goose.—Present at the end of the period in Dodge County (K. Burcar & B Domagalski) and reported on March 3 in Columbia (P. Ashman) County. Also reported in Ashland, Dane, Outagamie, St. Croix, Sheboygan, Taylor, and Winnebago Counties. A bird reported in Sheboygan County, May 24 (D. Tessen) was exceptionally late.

Ross' Goose.—Individuals of this species were reported from Columbia County, March 15–18 (multiple observers) and Dane County March 25–April 4 (multiple observers). All records were excepted by the Records Committee.

Canada Goose.—Present at the beginning of the period in Columbia, Dane, Dodge, Outagamie, Sauk, and Taylor Counties.

Wood Duck.—Present at the beginning of the period in Dane, Milwaukee, Walworth, Waupaca, and Winnebago Counties. On March 2, 41 birds were sighted in Dane County (A. & S. Shea).

Green-winged Teal.—Present at the beginning of the period in Dodge, and Vernon Counties. On April 12, 167 birds were sighted in Vernon County (J. Dankert).

American Black Duck.—Present at the beginning of period throughout the state.

Mallard.—Present at the beginning of period throughout the state. On March 28, 5,000+ birds were sighted in Dane County (A. & S. Shea).

Northern Pintail.—Present at the beginning of the period in Columbia, Dane, and Dodge Counties.

Blue-winged Teal.—First reported in Columbia and Dane Counties, March 20 (K. Burcar). On April 22, 120 birds were sighted in Columbia County (P. Ashman).

Cinnamon Teal.—Individuals of this species were reported as follows: Columbia County, April 22–27 (multiple observers); Dodge County, May 6–10 (multiple observers); Jefferson County, May 14 (K. Hale). All reports were accepted by the Records Committee. An additional report of a bird in Burnett County, May 3–11 is pending Committee review.

Northern Shoveler.—Present at the beginning of period in Dane and Milwaukee Counties (several observers). On April 4, 480 birds were sighted in Dane County (A. & S. Shea).

Gadwall.—Present at the beginning of the period in Columbia, Dane, Dodge, and Milwaukee Counties.

Eurasian Widgeon.—The report of a male observed in Dane County, March 8–16 (multiple observers) was accepted by the Records Committee.

American Widgeon.—Present at the beginning of the period in Columbia, Dane, Dodge, Milwaukee, Outagamie, and Waupaca

Counties. On April 7, 90 birds were sighted in Columbia County (P. Ashman).

Canvasback.—Present at the beginning of the period in Dane, and Walworth Counties. On April 3, 250 birds were sighted in Winnebago County (D. Tessen).

Redhead.—Present at the beginning of the period in Columbia, Dane, Manitowoc, and Walworth Counties.

Ring-necked Duck.—Present at the beginning of the period in Columbia, Dane, Walworth, and Waupaca Counties. On March 15, 1,100+ birds were sighted in Dane County (A. & S. Shea).

Greater Scaup.—Present at the beginning of the period the Lake Michigan shoreline as far north as Door County. On March 16, 4,000+ birds were sighted in Milwaukee County (M. Bontly).

Lesser Scaup.—Present at the beginning of the period in Columbia, Dane, Milwaukee, Vernon, and Walworth Counties. On April 4, 2,156 birds were sighted in Dane County (A. & S. Shea).

Harlequin Duck.—Reported as follows: Milwaukee County, BOP (M. Korducki); and Sheboygan County, May 17–24 (multiple observers).

Oldsquaw.—Present at the beginning of the period the Lake Michigan shoreline as far north as Door County. Late sightings reported as follows: Dane County, May 17 (R. Hoffman and A. Shea); and Milwaukee County, May 17–18 (S. Diehl and M. Korducki).

Black Scoter.—For whatever reason, all of this spring's reports occurred in mid–May: Ashland County, May 15–20 (D. Verch); Manitowoc County, May 16 (J. Frank); and Sheboygan County, May 17 (Jeff Baumann). A rare inland sighting of this species occurred in Dodge County, May 15–17 (R. Hoffman and A. & S. Shea).

Surf Scoter.—Reported as follows: Milwaukee County, BOP–March 15 (M. Korducki & T. Schultz); and Ashland County, May 11–19 (D. Verch).

White-winged Scoter.—For the second spring in a row, this species was scarce with only two reports: Sheboygan County, April 12 (Jeff Baumann); and Ozaukee County, May 1 (D. Gustafson).

Common Goldeneye.—Present at the beginning of period throughout the state.

Bufflehead.—Present at the beginning of the period in Columbia, Dane, Door, Milwaukee, and Sheboygan Counties. On April 4, 95 birds were sighted in Dane County (A. & S. Shea).

Hooded Merganser.—Present at the beginning of the period in Dane, Manitowoc, Milwaukee, Outagamie, Sauk, and Vernon Counties. On March 21, 407 birds were sighted in Columbia County (D. Tessen).

Common Merganser.—Present at the beginning of the period throughout the state.

Red-breasted Merganser.—Present at the beginning of the period in Door, Manitowoc, and Milwaukee Counties. On April 26, 2,500+ birds were sighted in Sheboygan County (D. & M. Brasser). A very late bird was present at the end of the period in Milwaukee County.

Ruddy Duck.—Present at the beginning of the period in Milwaukee, and Winnebago Counties. On April 16, 1,500+ birds were sighted in Green Lake County (T. Schultz).

Turkey Vulture.—First reported in Walworth County, March 2 (P. Parsons).

Osprey.—First reported in Marathon County, April 11 (D. Belter).

Swallow-tailed Kite.—An individual reported in Marquette County, May 12 (R. Ratering) was accepted by the Records Committee.

Bald Eagle.—Present at the beginning of period throughout the state. On March 8, 57 birds were sighted in Trempealeau County (T. Hunter).

Northern Harrier.—Present at the beginning of the period in Columbia, Dane, Dodge, Fond du Lac, and Monroe Counties. Reported at the end of the period in 17 counties.

Sharp-shinned Hawk.—Present at the beginning of the period in Dane, Door, Douglas, Fond du Lac, Milwaukee, Oconto, Outagamie, Polk, and Taylor Counties. On May 1, 35 birds were sighted in Ozaukee County (D. Gustafson). Present at the end of the period in Ashland, Barron, Door, Douglas, Fond du Lac, Marathon, Oconto, Polk, Price, Taylor, Vilas, and Walworth Counties.

Cooper's Hawk.—Present at the beginning of the period in Dane, Dodge, Green Lake, Jefferson, Milwaukee, Monroe, and Richland Counties. On May 1, 19 birds were sighted in Ozaukee County (D. Gustafson).

Northern Goshawk.—Present at the beginning of the period in Ashland, Door, Douglas, Marathon, and Taylor Counties. Reported during the period in Ashland, Clark, Dane, La-Crosse, Milwaukee, Outagamie, Portage, Price, Shawano, Vernon, and Vilas Counties. Present at the end of the period in Ashland, Door, Douglas, Marathon, Oconto, and Taylor Counties.

Red-shouldered Hawk.—Present at the beginning of the period in Fond du Lac and Portage Counties. This species was reported as far north as: Burnett, Door, Oconto, Polk, Shawano, Taylor, and Vilas Counties.

Broad-winged Hawk.—First reported in Sauk County, April 5 (A. & S. Shea). On April 20, 242 birds were sighted in Shawano County (Jeff Baumann).

Swainson's Hawk.—The only report of this species was of one bird in Dane County, May 26 (S. Robbins).

Red-tailed Hawk.—Present during the period throughout the state.

Rough-legged Hawk.—Late sightings reported as follows: Burnett County, May 18 (J. Hoefler) and Douglas County, May 25 (S. LaValley). On March 15, 32 birds were sighted in Oconto County (J. & K. Smith).

Golden Eagle.—Reported as follows: Oconto County, April 8 (J. & K. Smith) and Pierce County, April 10 (N. Carlson).

American Kestrel.—Present during the period throughout the state.

Merlin.—First reported in Douglas County, April 11 (R. Johnson). On May 1, 4 birds were sighted in Ozaukee County (D. Gustafson). Also reported during the period in Ashland, Calumet, Dane, Green Lake, Manitowoc, Marathon, Ozaukee, Portage, Sawyer, Shawano, Sheboygan, and Vilas Counties.

Peregrine Falcon.—Reported as follows: Dane & Milwaukee Counties, TTP (multiple observers); Douglas County, March 21 (R. Johnson); Douglas County, March 28 (R. Perala); Dunn County, April 16 (J. Polk); Portage County, April 22–May 2 (M. Berner); Burnett County, April 25–May 26 (J. Hoefler and R. Hoffman); Sheboygan County, April 25–May 15 (multiple observers); Trempealeau County, May 12 (T. Hunter); Manitowoc County, May 15 (C. Rudy); Monroe County, May 17 (D. Kuecherer); Dodge County, May 19 (S. Diehl); Manitowoc County, May 25 (C. Sontag).

Gyrfalcon.— A report of an individual in Bayfield County, April 1 (B. Bacon) was accepted by the Records Committee.

Gray Partridge.—Reported during the period in the following counties: Columbia, Dodge, Dane, Iowa, Manitowoc, Outagamie, Rock, and St. Croix Counties.

Ring-necked Pheasant.—Present throughout the period at the beginning of period throughout the state.

Spruce Grouse.—There were no reports of this species for the second spring in a row.

Ruffed Grouse.—Present during the period throughout the state but in very low numbers.

Greater Prairie-Chicken.—Reported during the period in Marathon, Portage, and Taylor Counties.

Sharp-tailed Grouse.—Reported during the period in Ashland, Burnett, Douglas, Price, and Taylor Counties.

Wild Turkey.—This species was reported as far north as: Burnett, Door, Pierce, Polk, Portage, and Shawano Counties.

Northern Bobwhite.—Reported during

the period in Columbia, Dane, Green Lake, Iowa, Lafayette, Monroe, Richland, Taylor, Trempealeau, and Winnebago Counties.

Yellow Rail.—Reported as follows: Green Lake County, May 1–17, up to 7 birds (multiple observers); Dodge County, May 16, 3–5 birds (multiple observers); Manitowoc County, May 17 (C. Rudy); Oconto County, May 23 (B. Mead); and Burnett County, May 29 (D. Tessen). A most unusual occurrence was of remains of a Yellow Rail found in an active nest box of Peregrine Falcons on the State Capitol Building in early May (fide R. Hoffman).

King Rail.—Reported as follows: Dodge County, April 24–May 23 (multiple observers); Columbia County, May 16–17 (T. Schultz); Dane County, May 17 (R. Hoffman & A. Shea); Manitowoc County, May 17 (C. Rudy); Waukesha County, May 19 (S. Diehl); and Trempealeau County, May 25 (R. Hoffman & M. Peterson).

Virginia Rail.—Present at the end of the period in Green Lake County (T. Schultz). The first migrant was reported in Dodge County, April 11 (K. Burcar).

Sora.—First reported on April 21 in Dane (P. Ashman) and Winnebago (D. Nussbaum) Counties.

Common Moorhen.—Reported as follows: Dodge County, April 23–May 15 (multiple observers); Oconto County, April 27–May 22 (J. & K. Smith); Waukesha County, May 4 (S. Diehl); and Winnebago County, May 9 (D. Tessen & T. Ziebell). On May 21, 40 birds were sighted in Trempealeau County (R. Hoffman).

American Coot.—Present at the beginning of the period in Dane, Milwaukee, Walworth and Waupaca Counties. On April 19, 1,000 birds were sighted in Dane County (P. Ashman).

Sandhill Crane.—First reported in Dane County, March 2 (A. & S. Shea). On May 9, 144 birds were sighted in Winnebago County (T. Ziebell).

Black-bellied Plover.—An excellent year for this species with reports as follows: Dodge County, April 12 (M. Korducki)—*a record early date!*; Dodge County, May 9–30 (multiple observers); Dane County, May 11 (K. Burcar); Trempealeau County, May 13 (T. Hunter);

Douglas County, May 14-EOP (R. Johnson & S. Robbins); Door County, May 20 (S. LaValley); Manitowoc County, May 22–28 (C. Sontag); Burnett County, May 27 (A. & S. Shea); Marathon County, May 30 (D. Belter); and Vilas County, May 30 (Jeff Baumann & Jim Baughman). On May 19, 24 birds were sighted in Dodge County (D. Belter).

Lesser Golden Plover.—An excellent year for this species with reports as follows: Dunn County, March 17 (J. Polk)—*a record early date!*; Ozaukee County, April 19–May 12 (J. Frank); Dodge County, April 23–May 23 (multiple observers); Trempealeau County, May 11 (T. Hunter); Columbia County, May 13 (S. Robbins); and Burnett County, May 27 (A. & S. Shea). On April 29, 19 birds were sighted in Dodge County (B. Domagalski).

Snowy Plover.—A report of an individual in Marinette County, May 12 (J. Smith) was accepted by the Records Committee.

Semipalmated Plover.—First reported in Dodge County, May 6 (B. Domagalski). Present at the end of the period in Ashland, Barron, Dane, Douglas, and Monroe Counties.

Piping Plover.—An encouraging 3 reports were received for this species this spring: Manitowoc County, May 2 (M. Peterson); Ashland County, May 7 (D. Verch); and Douglas County, May 17 (L. Semo).

Killdeer.—Present at beginning of period in 9 counties, as far north as Oconto and Trempealeau Counties.

American Avocet.—The only report of this species received this spring was of one bird in Manitowoc County, April 29 (C. Sontag).

Greater Yellowlegs.—First reported in Ashland County, March 20 (D. Verch). On May 12, 45 birds were sighted in Dane County (K. Burcar). Present at the end of the period in Burnett and Marathon Counties.

Lesser Yellowlegs.—First reported in Ashland County, March 21 (D. Verch). On April 21, 240 birds were sighted in Dodge County (B. Domagalski). Present at the end of the period in Burnett County.

Solitary Sandpiper.—First reported in Columbia County, April 23 (K. Burcar). Present at the end of the period in Ashland and Oconto Counties.

Willet.—Only two reports of this species were received this spring: Ozaukee County, May 4 (B. Domagalski) and Milwaukee County, May 19 (D. Gustafson).

Spotted Sandpiper.—First reported in Milwaukee County, April 16 (S. Diehl). On May 11, 21 birds were sighted in Douglas County (R. Johnson).

Upland Sandpiper.—First reported in Portage County, April 25 (M. Berner). On May 25, 9 birds were sighted in Portage County (M. Berner).

Whimbrel.—Reported as follows: Manitowoc County, May 15–21 (multiple observers); Door County, May 21 (K. Burcar); Kewaunee County, May 23 (A. & S. Shea); Door County, May 25 (fide R. & C. Lukes); and Bayfield County, May 26 (D. Verch). On May 21, 43 birds were sighted in Manitowoc County (C. Sontag).

Hudsonian Godwit.—A good spring for this species with reports as follows: Columbia County, May 10–11 (B. Boldt & K. Burcar); Dane County, May 13–16 (K. Burcar and A. & S. Shea); Trempealeau County, May 13–15 (T. Hunter); Dodge County, May 15–30 (multiple observers); Shawano County, May 15–18 (M. Peterson); Jefferson County, May 17 (K. Hale); St. Croix County, May 23 (R. Hoffman); Dunn County, May 24 (J. Polk); Monroe County, May 25 (E. Epstein); Burnett County, May 26–29 (J. Hoefler). On May 26, 20 birds were sighted in Burnett County (R. Hoffman & M. Peterson).

Marbled Godwit.—Reported as follows: Milwaukee County, April 24 (D. Gustafson); Manitowoc County, May 18 (D. Belter); Dunn County, May 24 (J. Polk); Dodge County, May 26 (S. Diehl); St. Croix County, May 26 (R. Hoffman and M. Peterson); and Burnett County, May 27 (A. & S. Shea).

Ruddy Turnstone.—First reported in Manitowoc County, May 1 (C. Sontag). On May 22, 950 birds were sighted in Manitowoc County (C. Sontag). Present at the end of the period in Douglas, Marathon, and Winnebago Counties.

Red Knot.—Reported as follows: Manitowoc County, May 23-EOP (A. & S. Shea and C. Sontag); Douglas County, May 25-EOP (M. Peterson & L. Semo); and Burnett County, May 26 (R. Hoffman).

Sanderling.—First reported in Manitowoc County, May 3 (C. Sontag). Present at the end of the period in Ashland, Douglas, Manitowoc, and Winnebago Counties.

Semipalmated Sandpiper.—First reported in Vernon County, May 9 (J. Dankert). On May 29, 75 birds were sighted in Dane County (P. Ashman). Present at the end of the period in Ashland, Dane, Douglas, Manitowoc, Oconto, and Vilas Counties.

Western Sandpiper.—Reported as follows: Dodge County, May 16–24 (D. Gustafson & F. Lesher); St. Croix County, May 17 (P. Risch); Brown County, May 18 (M. Peterson); and Washburn County, May 25 (M. Peterson).

Least Sandpiper.—First reported in Dane County, May 2 (K. Burcar and A. & S. Shea). On May 11, 130 birds were sighted in Dane County (K. Burcar). Present at the end of the period in Ashland, Burnett, Dane, Marathon, Oconto, and Vilas Counties.

White-rumped Sandpiper.—First reported in Manitowoc County, May 10 (C. Rudy). Present at the end of the period in Ashland, Dane, Dodge, and Manitowoc Counties.

Baird's Sandpiper.—First reported in Calumet County, May 9 (C. Rudy). Also reported during the period in Ashland, Chippewa, Dodge, Milwaukee, St. Croix, and Sawyer Counties.

Pectoral Sandpiper.—First reported in Dane County, March 26 (K. Burcar). On April 24, 158 birds were sighted in Dodge County (K. Burcar). Present at the end of the period in Ashland, Dane, and Oconto Counties.

Purple Sandpiper.—Reported in Sheboygan County, BOP–March 28 (D. & M. Brasser and K. Burcar). Record pending review by the Records Committee.

Dunlin.—First reported in Dodge County, April 15 (B. Domagalski). On May 21, 725 birds were sighted in Dodge County (B. Domagalski).

Present at the end of the period in Dane, Douglas, Manitowoc, Marathon, Monroe, Vilas, and Winnebago Counties.

Stilt Sandpiper.—There were no reports of this species this spring.

Ruff.—There were no reports of this species this spring.

Short-billed Dowitcher.—First reported in Dodge County, April 4 (D. Nussbaum). On May 12, 40 birds were sighted in Dane County (K. Burcar). Present at the end of the period in Manitowoc County (C. Sontag).

Long-billed Dowitcher.—First reported in Dodge County, April 15–22 (K. Burcar & B. Domagalski)

Common Snipe.—First reported in Dane County, March 17 (P. Ashman). On April 19, 35 birds were sighted in Oconto County (J. & K. Smith).

American Woodcock.—Present at the beginning of the period in Milwaukee County (S. Diehl) and March 3, Dane County (A. & S. Shea).

Wilson's Phalarope.—First reported in Columbia County, May 6 (P. Ashman). On May 27, 35 birds were sighted in Burnett County (A. & S. Shea).

Red-necked Phalarope.—There were no reports of this species this spring.

Laughing Gull.—The following reports of this species were accepted by the Records Committee: Manitowoc County, May 12 (C. Rudy) and Burnett County, May 29 (B. Boldt & M. Korducki).

Franklin's Gull.—An excellent spring for this species with reports as follows: LaCrosse County, March 8 (J. Dankert)—*a record early date!*; Dodge County, April 15–16 (K. Burcar); Vernon County, April 18 (J. Dankert); Milwaukee County, April 26–May 24 (multiple observers); Sheboygan County, April 26 (K. Burcar) and May 15–23 (A. & S. Shea); Chippewa County, May 19–23 (J. Polk); and Marinette County, May 23 (B. Mead).

Little Gull.—Reported as follows: Manitowoc County, May 3-EOP (C. Rudy & C. Sontag); Milwaukee County, May 5–18 (D. Gustafson & M. Korducki); and a very rare inland record in Chippewa County, May 13 (J. Polk).

Bonaparte's Gull.—First reported in Milwaukee County, March 15 (B. Boldt & K. Burcar). On April 20, 12,000 birds were sighted in Milwaukee County (B. Boldt).

Ring-billed Gull.—Present at the beginning of the period along the Lake Michigan shoreline.

Herring Gull.—Present at the beginning of the period along the Great Lakes' shorelines.

Thayer's Gull.—Reported as follows: Milwaukee County, BOP–March 15 (K. Burcar & M. Korducki); Manitowoc County, March 15 (K. Burcar); and Douglas County, May 25 (M. Peterson).

Iceland Gull.—The following reports of this species were accepted by the Records Committee: Milwaukee County, March 13 (B. Boldt); Milwaukee County, March 14–15 (B. Boldt & T. Schultz); Manitowoc County, March 29 (D. Tessen); Milwaukee County, April 14 (B. Domagalski); Douglas County, April 16 (R. Johnson); and Chippewa County, April 17 (J. Polk).

Lesser Black-backed Gull.—The report of an individual in Sheboygan County, April 5 (B. Boldt) was accepted by the Records Committee.

Glaucous Gull.—Reported as follows: Douglas County, BOP–May 11 (R. Johnson); Manitowoc County, BOP-April 11 (C. Sontag); Milwaukee County, BOP-April 10 (multiple observers); Winnebago County, BOP–May 9 (D. Nussbaum & T. Ziebell); Sheboygan County, March 20 (D. & M. Brasser); and Ozaukee County, April 5 (B. Boldt). On March 10, 8 birds were sighted in Manitowoc County (C. Sontag).

Great Black-backed Gull.—The following reports of this species were accepted by the Records Committee: Reported as follows: Ashland County, April 16 (D. Verch) and Sheboygan County, May 23 (M. Korducki & B. Boldt).

Caspian Tern.—First reported in Milwaukee County, April 8 (B. Boldt).

Common Tern.—First reported in Milwaukee County, April 15 (B. Boldt). On May 5, 500 birds were sighted in Milwaukee County (D. Gustafson).

Forster's Tern.—First reported in Manitowoc County, April 10 (C. Sontag). On April 28, 150 birds were sighted in Milwaukee County (B. Boldt). This species was reported as far north as Ashland and Douglas Counties.

Black Tern.—First reported in Waukesha County, April 21 (B. Boldt).

Rock Dove.—Present during the period throughout the state.

Mourning Dove.—Present during the period throughout the state.

Black-billed Cuckoo.—First reported in Milwaukee County, May 11 (B. Boldt). On May 17, 6 birds were sighted in Walworth County (P. Ashman).

Yellow-billed Cuckoo.—First reported in Milwaukee County, May 4 (S. Diehl).

Eastern Screech-Owl.—This species was reported as far north as Barron and Taylor Counties.

Great Horned Owl.—Present during the period throughout the state.

Snowy Owl.—This species staged one of its most impressive invasions in recent memory with observations of one or more owls in the following counties: Ashland, Brown, Burnett, Dane, Dodge, Douglas, Eau Claire, Oconto, Outagamie, Pierce, Shawano, Taylor, and Winnebago Counties. On March 5, 10 birds were sighted in Douglas County (S. LaValley).

Northern Hawk-Owl.—A report of an individual in Ashland County, March 3 (M. Spreeman) was accepted by the Records Committee.

Barred Owl.—Present during the period throughout the state.

Great Gray Owl.—Reported in Douglas County, May 18 (S. Robbins). Record pending review by the Records Committee.

Long-eared Owl.—This spring topped the last two springs and provided further evidence that this elusive owl may be more widespread than realized. Reported as follows: Portage County, March 7 (M. Peterson); Oconto County, March 23–May 16 (J. & K. Smith); Dane County, March 21 (D. Tessen); Columbia County, May 17 (Jeff Baumann & T. Schultz); Taylor County, May 17 (P. Risch); and two sightings in Douglas County, May 22, nest (L. Semo) and May 26 (R. Johnson).

Short-eared Owl.—Reported as follows: Milwaukee County, BOP–May 1 (B. Domagalski & M. Korducki); Oconto County, BOP–April 12 (J. & K. Smith); Pierce County, March 27 (N. Carlson); Calumet County, April 11 (C. Rudy); Clark County, May 17 (P. Risch); and Dodge County, May 23 (A. & S. Shea).

Northern Saw-whet Owl.—Reported as follows: Dane County, March 1 (A. & S. Shea) and March 21 (D. Tessen); Portage County, BOP–April 7 (L. Semo); Ashland County, March 4–EOP (D. Verch); Douglas County, March 9-EOP (multiple observers); Sheboygan County, March 11 (the Kuhn Family); Marathon County, March 13 (D. Belter); Vilas County, March 16 (B. Reardon); Milwaukee County, March 21–April 7 (M. Bontly & S. Diehl); Portage County, April 11–17 (M. Berner); Sawyer County, April 25–26 (K. Merkel); Taylor County, May 6 (P. Risch); Trempealeau County, May 20 (R. Hoffman); Burnett County, May 29 (D. Tessen); Forest County, May 29 (T. Schultz); Vilas County, May 30 (Jeff Baumann & Jim Baughman); and Price County, May 31, nest (M. Hardy). The Linwood Station banding operation in Portage County banded a total of 102 saw-whet owls during the season with a high of 18 on March 21 (E. Jacobs).

Common Nighthawk.—First reported in LaCrosse County, May 1 (J. Dankert).

Whip-poor-will.—First reported in Manitowoc County, April 20 (C. Sontag).

Chimney Swift.—First reported in Dane County, April 19 (P. Ashman).

Ruby-throated Hummingbird.—First

reported in Dane County, April 24 (M. Evanson). On May 17, a remarkable migration of 300+ birds was witnessed in Bayfield County (L. Cowles).

Belted Kingfisher.—Present at the beginning of the period in Columbia, Dane, Manitowoc, Milwaukee, Monroe, Pierce, Richland, and Trempealeau Counties.

Red-headed Woodpecker.—Present at the beginning of the period in Columbia, Dane, LaCrosse, Monroe, Taylor, Trempealeau, and Vernon Counties.

Red-bellied Woodpecker.—Present at beginning of period in a remarkable 24 Counties, as far north as Barron, Door, Douglas!, Marathon, Oconto, Polk, and Taylor Counties.

Yellow-bellied Sapsucker.—First reported in Dane County, March 21 (P. Ashman). On April 7, 19 birds were sighted in Dane County (P. Ashman).

Downy Woodpecker.—Present during the period throughout the state.

Hairy Woodpecker.—Present during the period throughout the state.

Black-backed Woodpecker.—Reported as follows: Sawyer County, April 26 (K. Merkel); Vilas County, May 10–31 (Jeff Baumann & Jim Baughman); and Price County, May 27 (M. Hardy).

Northern Flicker.—Present at the beginning of the period in Dane, Dodge, Monroe, Richland, and Sauk Counties. On April 20, 32 birds were sighted in Dane County (P. Ashman).

Pileated Woodpecker.—Present during the period throughout the state.

Olive-sided Flycatcher.—First reported on May 2 in Milwaukee (R. Gutschow); and Rock (B. Domagalski) Counties.

Eastern Wood Pewee.—First reported in Grant County, May 3 (K. Burcar and A. & S. Shea).

Yellow-bellied Flycatcher.—First reported in Milwaukee County, May 12 (J. Frank & D. Gustafson). On May 23, 30+ birds were sighted in Sheboygan and Manitowoc Counties (A. & S. Shea).

Acadian Flycatcher.—There were twice as many locations for this species in 1992 as there was the past two springs. First reported in Rock County, May 3 (Jeff Baumann). Also reported during the period in Dane, Fond du Lac, Green Lake, Jefferson, Milwaukee, Monroe, Ozaukee, Pepin, Sauk, Walworth, Washington and Waukesha Counties.

Alder Flycatcher.—First reported in Taylor County, May 11 (B. Armbrust).

Willow Flycatcher.—First reported in Taylor County, May 3 (B. Armbrust), *tieing the record early arrival date!*

Least Flycatcher.—First reported May 1 in Green Lake (T. Schultz) and Portage (M. Berner) Counties. On May 16, 19+ birds were sighted in Marathon County (D. Belter).

Eastern Phoebe.—First reported in Ozaukee County, March 8 (B. Boldt).

Vermilion Flycatcher.—A report of an individual in Waukesha County, May 11 (M. Welnak) was accepted by the Records Committee. This constitutes the third accepted record for this species in the state.

Great-crested Flycatcher.—First reported in Dane County, April 20 (P. Ashman).

Western Kingbird.—Reported as follows: Portage County, May 22 (G. Stout); and Bayfield County, May 30 (multiple observers).

Eastern Kingbird.—First reported on May 1 in Door (S. Dee), Marathon (D. Belter), and Milwaukee (D. Gustafson) Counties.

Horned Lark.—Present during the period throughout the state.

Purple Martin.—First reported in Dodge County, April 11 (K. Burcar & B. Domagalski).

Tree Swallow.—First reported in Dodge County, March 5 (B. Domagalski). A record on March 8 in Dunn County (J. Polk) was noteworthy. On April 22, 2,000 birds were sighted in Marathon County (D. Belter).

Rough-winged Swallow.—First reported in Dane County, April 7 (S. Robbins).

Bank Swallow.—First reported in Vernon County, April 12 (J. Dankert).

Cliff Swallow.—First reported in Portage County, April 14 (M. Berner). On May 24, 1,470 birds were sighted in Portage County (M. Berner).

Barn Swallow.—First reported in Dane County, April 6 (A. & S. Shea).

Gray Jay.—Reported as follows: Ashland County, TTP (T. Hunter & T. Soulen); Douglas County, TTP (R. Johnson & T. Soulen); Price County, TTP (M. Hardy); Taylor County, BOP–March 17 (B. Armbrust) and May 17 (P. Risch); Vilas County, March 2–May 30 (Jim Baughman, J. Dankert, & B. Reardon); Forest County, April 11 (D. Tessen); Sawyer County, April 25 (K. Merkel); and Oneida County, May 29 (T. Schultz).

Black-billed Magpie.—A report of an individual in Columbia County, May 2 (D. Gustafson) was accepted by the Records Committee.

Blue Jay.—Present during the period throughout the state.

American Crow.—Present during the period throughout the state.

Common Raven.—This species was reported as far south as: Door, Marathon, Monroe, Outagamie, Portage, and Shawano Counties.

Black-capped Chickadee.—Present during the period throughout the state.

Boreal Chickadee.—Reported as follows: Lincoln County, March 12, 7 birds (R. Hoffman); Sawyer County, April 25–26 (K. Merkel); Vilas County, May 10–30 (Jim Baughman); Forest County, May 29 (M. Peterson & T. Schultz); and Oneida County, May 29 (T. Schultz).

Tufted Titmouse.—Present at the beginning of the period in Columbia, Dane, and Sauk Counties. Also reported during the period in Crawford, Grant, Lafayette, Rock, and Vernon Counties. This species was reported as far north as Monroe, and St. Croix Counties.

Red-breasted Nuthatch.—Present during the period throughout the state. On April 1, 40 birds were sighted in Oneida County (D. Tessen).

White-breasted Nuthatch.—Present during the period throughout the state.

Brown Creeper.—Present during the period throughout the state. On May 3, 20 birds were sighted in Ozaukee County (D. Tessen).

Carolina Wren.—Another good showing for this species with Reported as follows: Door County, BOP–April 26 (S. Dee); Dane County, March 16-EOP (multiple observers); Iowa County, March 21 (K. Burcar); Racine County, March 22 (F. Lesher); Manitowoc County, April 19 (K. Burcar & D. Tessen); and Grant County, May 3–5 (P. Ashman & K. Burcar).

House Wren.—First reported in Dane County, April 21 (P. Ashman).

Winter Wren.—First reported in Dane County, March 25 (K. Burcar).

Sedge Wren.—First reported in Green Lake County, May 1 (T. Schultz).

Marsh Wren.—First reported in Dodge County, April 24 (K. Burcar).

Golden-crowned Kinglet.—Present at the end of the period in Oconto, Portage, and Winnebago Counties. The first apparent migrant was observed March 8 in Jefferson County (K. Hale). The only report at the end of the period came from Vilas County.

Ruby-crowned Kinglet.—First reported in Dane County, April 6 (K. Burcar). Present at the end of the period in Vilas County.

Blue-gray Gnatcatcher.—First reported on April 19 in Dane (P. Ashman) and Manitowoc (K. Burcar) Counties. This species was reported as far north as: Burnett!, Door, Douglas!, Marathon!, Oconto, and Polk Counties. Evidence from the past several springs suggests that this species is slowly expanding its range northward.

Eastern Bluebird.—Present at the beginning of the period in Dane, Dodge, Milwaukee, Monroe, Racine, Richland, and Walworth Counties.

Veery.—First reported in Milwaukee County, May 2 (multiple observers). On May 15, 30 birds were sighted in Dane County (R. Hoffman and A. & S. Shea).

Gray-cheeked Thrush.—First reported in Ashland County, April 21 (D. Verch). On May 17, 40 birds were sighted in Dane County (R. Hoffman & A. Shea).

Swainson's Thrush.—First reported in Ashland County, April 26 (D. Verch). On May 15, 30 birds were sighted in Dane County (R. Hoffman and A. & S. Shea).

Hermit Thrush.—First reported on April 6 in Dane (K. Burcar); LaCrosse (J. Dankert); and Milwaukee (N. Zehner) Counties. On April 16, 50 birds were sighted in Milwaukee County (N. Zehner).

Wood Thrush.—First reported in Rock County, April 25 (D. Tessen).

American Robin.—Present at the beginning of the period in 17 counties as far north as Ashland, Oconto, Polk and Portage Counties. On March 21, 700+ birds were sighted in Dane County (D. Tessen).

Gray Catbird.—First reported in Milwaukee County, April 16 (S. Diehl). On May 12, 30 birds were sighted in Dane County (P. Ashman).

Northern Mockingbird.—A good spring for this extralimital species. Reported as follows: Winnebago County, April 1–5 (multiple observers); Dane County, April 24 (P. Ashman) and April 30 (D. Cederstom); Manitowoc County, April 26–27 (C. Sontag); Oconto County, May 12 (J. & K. Smith); and Burnett County, May 18 (J. Hoefler).

Brown Thrasher.—First reported on

April 19 in Manitowoc (K. Burcar) and Portage (M. Berner) Counties.

Water Pipit.—Reported as follows: Dodge County, April 16–18 (K. Burcar & B. Domagalski); Milwaukee County, April 16–17 (M. Korducki); Oconto County, May 16 (J. & K. Smith); and Shawano County, May 16 (M. Peterson).

Bohemian Waxwing.—Reported as follows: Ashland County, BOP–April 5 (F. Lesher & D. Verch); Portage County, BOP–April 3 (M. Berner); Shawano County, March 12 (M. Peterson); and Marathon County, March 14–April 3 (D. Belter). On March 14, 95 birds were sighted in Marathon County (D. Belter).

Cedar Waxwing.—Present at the beginning of the period in Barron, Dane, Door, LaCrosse, Milwaukee, Outagamie, Polk, and Winnebago Counties.

Northern Shrike.—Fairly widespread throughout the state in March. Last reported in Taylor County, April 22 (B. Armbrust).

Loggerhead Shrike.—An encouraging number of reports as follows: Rock County, April 4 (S. & P. Kyle); Oconto County, April 12-EOP (multiple observers); Pierce County, April 14 (N. Carlson); Monroe County, April 17 (E. Epstein); Manitowoc County, April 20 (Jeff Baumann); Dane County, May 2 (A. Shea); and Green Lake County, EOP (Jeff Baumann).

European Starling.—Present during the period throughout the state.

White-eyed Vireo.—Reported as follows: Walworth County, April 25 (D. Tessen); Milwaukee County, May 2–4 (multiple observers); Dane County, May 11–12 (P. Ashman & K. Burcar); and Green County, May 23 (multiple observers).

Bell's Vireo.—While this spring's four records provided little optimism for this species status as threatened in Wisconsin, a "hot spot" for this species was discovered in Trempealeau County with 7 individuals being observed on May 21 (R. Hoffman). Single birds were reported in Dane County, May 16–30 (multiple observers); Iowa County, May 23 (K. Burcar); and LaCrosse County, May 26 (M. Peterson).

Solitary Vireo.—First reported in Columbia County, April 23 (K. Burcar). On May 2, 10 birds were sighted in Milwaukee County (B. Boldt).

Yellow-throated Vireo.—First reported in Dane County, April 30 (P. Ashman).

Warbling Vireo.—First reported in Green Lake County, May 1 (T. Schultz).

Philadelphia Vireo.—First reported in Milwaukee County, May 10 (K. Burcar & M. Korducki).

Red-eyed Vireo.—First reported in Dane County, May 2 (D. Lauten & K. Castelein).

Blue-winged Warbler.—First reported on May 2 in Dane (A. & S. Shea) and Milwaukee (R. Gutschow & M. Korducki) Counties.

Golden-winged Warbler.—First reported in Douglas County, April 28 (S. LaValley).

Tennessee Warbler.—First reported on May 2 in Dane (P. Ashman and (A. & S. Shea); Milwaukee (B. Boldt & M. Korducki); Outagamie (J. Anderson & S. Petznick); and Rock (K. Burcar) Counties.

Orange-crowned Warbler.—First reported in Dane County, April 25 (D. Lauten & K. Castelein).

Nashville Warbler.—First reported in Milwaukee County, April 25 (M. Korducki).

Northern Parula Warbler.—First reported on May 2 in Milwaukee (R. Gutschow) and Rock (K. Burcar) Counties.

Yellow Warbler.—First reported in Dane County, April 20 (P. Ashman).

Chestnut-sided Warbler.—First reported on May 2 in Dane (A. & S. Shea) and Milwaukee (multiple observers) Counties.

Magnolia Warbler.—First reported on May 2 in Dane (D. Lauten & K. Castelein); Mil-

waukee (multiple observers); and Rock (K. Burcar) Counties.

Cape May Warbler.—First reported in Dane County, May 9 (A. & S. Shea).

Black-throated Blue Warbler.—First reported in Walworth County, May 3 (D. Tessen). Also reported during the period in Dane, Forest, Marathon, Milwaukee, and Sauk Counties. On May 30, 4 birds were sighted in Bayfield County (T. Schultz).

Yellow-rumped Warbler.—Present at beginning of period in Dane County (K. Burcar). Many observers, however, reported their first observation of this bird between April 7 and April 12.

Black-throated Green Warbler.—First reported in Milwaukee County, April 29 (multiple observers).

Blackburnian Warbler.—First reported in Dane County, April 25 (D. Lauten & K. Castelein) *tieing the record early arrival date!*

Yellow-throated Warbler.—The following extralimital reports of this species were accepted by the Records Committee: Manitowoc County, May 6 (C. Sontag) and Grant County, May 25 (D. Tessen). There were 3 reports of this species at its traditional Avon Bottoms haunts in Rock County: April 29 (R. Hoffman); May 2 (K. Burcar); and May 8 (M. Peterson).

Pine Warbler.—First reported in Milwaukee County, April 17 (R. Gutschow).

Prairie Warbler.—The only report of this species was of one bird in Manitowoc County, May 23 (A. & S. Shea).

Palm Warbler.—First reported on April 19 in Dane (P. Ashman); Manitowoc (K. Burcar); and Milwaukee (B. Boldt) Counties. A very late sighting was of a bird in Dane County, May 28 (R. Hoffman).

Bay-breasted Warbler.—First reported in Portage County, May 2 (M. Berner).

Blackpoll Warbler.—First reported in Portage County, May 1 (M. Berner).

Cerulean Warbler.—First reported in Rock County, May 2 (K. Burcar). A report of a pair of birds in Vilas County, May 31 (Jeff Baumann & Jim Baughman) was extremely far north.

Black-and-white Warbler.—First reported in Milwaukee County, April 25 (M. Korducki).

American Redstart.—First reported in LaCrosse County, May 1 (J. Dankert).

Prothonotary Warbler.—First reported on May 3 in Dane (P. Ashman); Grant (K. Burcar and A. & S. Shea); and Milwaukee (B. Boldt & M. Korducki) Counties. Reported in 5 other counties during the period as far north as Monroe, Polk and St. Croix Counties.

Worm-eating Warbler.—Reported as follows: Milwaukee County, May 3–4 (D. Gustafson & M. Korducki); Manitowoc County, May 13 (C. Rudy); Dane County, May 17–18, (multiple observers); Grant County, May 23 (D. Tessen); Waukesha County, May 25 (D. Gustafson); and Sauk County, May 28, 3 birds (M. Peterson).

Ovenbird.—First reported on April 29 in Dane (K. Burcar) and Milwaukee (B. Boldt & D. Gustafson) Counties. On May 2, 50 birds were sighted in Milwaukee County (B. Boldt).

Northern Waterthrush.—First reported in Green Lake County, April 20 (T. Schultz).

Louisiana Waterthrush.—First reported on April 8 in Dane (P. Ashman) and Sauk (K. Burcar) Counties. Also reported during the period in Fond du Lac, Grant, Milwaukee, Pepin, and Shawano Counties.

Kentucky Warbler.—An extralimital reported of a bird in Douglas County! on May 1 (R. Johnson) *was a record early arrival date!* Also reported in: Grant County, May 8 (K. Burcar); Dane County, May 16–23 (P. Ashman & K. Burcar); and Pepin County, May 22 (R. Hoffman). On mAY 17, 14 birds were sighted in Grant County (D. Lauten & K. Castelein).

Connecticut Warbler.—First reported in Fond du Lac County, May 15 (R. Hoffman and A. & S. Shea). Present at the end of the period in Ashland, Burnett, Douglas, and Vilas Counties.

Mourning Warbler.—First reported in Grant County, May 3 (K. Burcar) *tieing the record early arrival date!.*

Common Yellowthroat.—First reported in Milwaukee County, April 20 (M. Korducki).

Hooded Warbler.—A good spring for this species with an above average number of sightings and at new locations. Reported as follows: Walworth County, May 9 (P. Ashman); Waukesha County, May 9 (T. Schultz); Dane County, May 11-EOP (multiple observers); Manitowoc County, May 13–16 (multiple observers); Waukesha County, May 24 (D. Tessen); Jefferson County, May 26, 3 birds (P. Ashman); and Pepin County, May 26–27 (A. & S. Shea).

Wilson's Warbler.—First reported on May 2 in Dane (P. Ashman); Green (K. Burcar); and Marathon (D. Belter) Counties.

Canada Warbler.—First reported in Milwaukee County, May 2 (M. Korducki).

Yellow-breasted Chat.—Reported as follows: Green Lake County, May 17 (Jeff Baumann & T. Schultz); Rock County, May 21–23 (R. Hoffman & D. Tessen); and Green County, May 23 (K. Burcar).

Summer Tanager.—Reported as follows: Milwaukee County, May 1–3 (multiple observers); Dane County, May 12 (E. Hansen) and May 17 (multiple observers); Brown County, May 13–18 (J. Knickelbine & M. Peterson); and Manitowoc County, May 19 (M. Berner).

Scarlet Tanager.—First reported in Douglas County, May 1 (R. Johnson).

Western Tanager.—A report of an individual in Fond du Lac County, May 16 (H. Riedner & D. Whitney) was accepted by the Records Committee.

Northern Cardinal.—Present at the beginning of the period in these northerly locations: Ashland, Barron, Door, Marathon, Oconto, Polk, Price, and Taylor Counties. On March 2, 32 birds were sighted in Dane County (K. Burcar). The cardinal, like the house finch and red-bellied woodpecker, appears to be close to colonizing the entire state.

Rose-breasted Grosbeak.—First reported on May 1 in Dane (P. Ashman & K. Burcar); Green Lake (T. Schultz); and Outagamie (D. Nussbaum) Counties.

Indigo Bunting.—First reported on May 1 in Outagamie (J. Anderson & S. Petznick) and Waushara (D. Nussbaum) Counties.

Dickcissel.—First reported in Dane County, May 15 (K. Burcar). Also reported during the period in Eau Claire, Iowa, Rock, St. Croix, Shawano, and Sheboygan Counties.

Rufous-sided Towhee.—First reported in Milwaukee County, March 22 (S. Diehl).

American Tree Sparrow.—Last reported in Vilas County, May 4 (Jim Baughman).

Chipping Sparrow.—First reported in Dane County, April 17 (K. Burcar).

Clay-colored Sparrow.—First reported in Marathon County, April 29 (D. Belter). On May 25, 23 birds were sighted in Portage County (M. Berner).

Field Sparrow.—First reported in Dane County, March 27 (S. Robbins).

Vesper Sparrow.—First reported in Portage County, March 24 (M. Berner).

Lark Sparrow.—First reported in Rock County, April 29 (R. Hoffman). Also reported during the period in Adams, Burnett, Dunn, Monroe, St. Croix, and Sauk Counties.

Savannah Sparrow.—First reported in Milwaukee County, March 17 (M. Korducki).

Grasshopper Sparrow.—First reported in Dane County, May 2 (A. & S. Shea).

Henslow's Sparrow.—First reported in Green Lake County, May 1 (T. Schultz). A good year for this species with observations in 12 counties compared to 8 and 7, respectively, for 1990 and 1991. In keeping with its semi-nomadic habitats, only one county—Green Lake—had observations in all 3 years, and only four other counties had observations in at least two

of the three springs—Richland, Rock, Shawano and Taylor Counties. Other observations of this species in spring, 1992 were in: Barron, Bayfield, Door, Iowa, Marquette, Outagamie, and Waukesha Counties.

LeConte's Sparrow.—First reported on May 2 in Marathon (D. Belter); and Ozaukee (B. Boldt & (M. Korducki) Counties. Unusually late sightings were in: Manitowoc County, May 16 (C. Rudy); Green Lake County, May 15–17 (multiple observers); Door County, May 21 (S. Peterson); and Ozaukee County, May 26 (S. Diehl). Present at the end of the period in Ashland, Burnett, Marathon, Taylor, and Vilas Counties.

Sharp-tailed Sparrow.—Reported as follows: Oconto County, May 21 (B. Mead) and Burnett County, May 25–29, up to 3 birds (multiple observers).

Fox Sparrow.—First reported on March 5 in LaCrosse (J. Dankert) and Rock (K. Burcar) Counties. On April 12, 33 birds were sighted in Portage County (M. Berner).

Song Sparrow.—Present at the beginning of the period in Columbia, Dane, Dodge, Jefferson, and Milwaukee Counties. On March 22, 250+ birds were sighted in Dane County (A. & S. Shea).

Lincoln's Sparrow.—First reported in Portage County, May 1 (M. Berner).

Swamp Sparrow.—Present at the beginning of the period in Dane, and Milwaukee Counties.

White-throated Sparrow.—Present at the beginning of the period in Dane, and Milwaukee Counties.

White-crowned Sparrow.—First reported in Walworth County, March 14 (D. Tessen). Present at the end of the period in Door County (R. & C. Lukes).

Harris' Sparrow.—A poor showing for this species this spring with only four reports: Walworth County, May 2 (D. Tessen); Taylor County, May 7–8 (P. Risch); LaCrosse County, May 10 (J. Dankert); and Douglas County, May 14–15 (R. Johnson).

Dark-eyed Junco.—Present at the end of the period in Taylor and Vilas Counties.

Lapland Longspur.—Late sightings reported as follows: Dane County, May 17 (R. Hoffman and A. Shea); Dodge County, May 17 (Jeff Baumann); and Manitowoc County, May 23 (A. & S. Shea).

Snow Bunting.—Present at the beginning of the period in Ashland, Barron, Burnett, Dodge, Door, Price, and Taylor Counties. Also reported during the period in Columbia, Portage, and Price Counties. On April 1, 1,000+ birds were sighted in Langlade County (D. Tessen). Last reported in Ashland County, May 10 (D. Verch).

Bobolink.—First reported in Waushara County, April 22 (D. Nussbaum).

Red-winged Blackbird.—Present at beginning of period in 17 Counties, as far north as Calumet, LaCrosse, Oconto, Outagamie, Shawano, Winnebago, and Wood Counties.

Eastern Meadowlark.—Present at the beginning of the period in Dane, Dodge, Dunn, Fond du Lac, Oconto, and Winnebago Counties.

Western Meadowlark.—First reported in Rock County, March 5 (K. Burcar).

Yellow-headed Blackbird.—First reported in Dodge County, April 5 (K. Burcar & B. Domagalski).

Rusty Blackbird.—Present at the beginning of the period in Columbia, Dane, and LaCrosse Counties. Late sightings were reported as follows: Milwaukee County, May 10 (B. Domagalski & M. Korducki) and Dodge County, May 12 (S. Diehl).

Brewer's Blackbird.—Present at the beginning of the period in Columbia and Dane Counties.

Common Grackle.—Present at beginning of period in 16 Counties, as far north as LaCrosse, Monroe, Outagamie, Trempealeau, and Winnebago Counties.

Brown-headed Cowbird.—Present at the

beginning of the period in Columbia, Dane, Dodge, Iowa, Milwaukee, Monroe, and Winnebago Counties.

Orchard Oriole.—First reported in Dane County, May 2 (P. Ashman). R. Hoffman reports 21 pairs of this species in various spots in southern Wisconsin, 7 pairs of which were in Dane County. This species was reported as far north as: Ashland, Dunn, Pepin, and Wood Counties.

Northern Oriole.—First reported on May 1 in Dane (K. Burcar); Douglas (S. LaValley); Jefferson (K. Burcar); Outagamie (J. Anderson, S. Petznick, & D. Nussbaum); and Rock (K. Burcar) Counties. On May 20, an amazing 600–700 birds were counted in about 2 hours near Cornucopia in Bayfield County (L. Cowles); possibly the result of a "blocking" effect by Lake Superior on northward migrants.

Pine Grosbeak.—Reported as follows: Ashland County, BOP–March 22 (D. Verch); Douglas County, March 1 (R. Perala); Taylor County, BOP–March 14 (B. Armbrust); Vilas County, March 5 (Jim Baughman); Forest County, March 12 (B. Reardon) and April 1 (D. Tessen); and Lincoln County, March 12 (R. Hoffman).

Purple Finch.—Present at the end of the period in Ashland, Barron, Door, Douglas, Price, Taylor, and Vilas Counties.

House Finch.—Present throughout the state throughout the period. This year the house finch "finished off" the state by moving into Bayfield and Douglas Counties.

Red Crossbill.—Only two reports of this wanderer this spring: Vilas County, April 20–22 (Jeff Baumann & Jim Baughman) and Douglas County, May 31 (S. Robbins & D. Tessen).

White-winged Crossbill.—Only three reports of this boreal species this spring: Price County, March 14 (M. Hardy); Douglas County, March 21 (R. Perala); and Forest County, April 1 (D. Tessen).

Common Redpoll.—Present at beginning of period in 18 Counties, as far south as Dane, Milwaukee, and Monroe Counties. On March 27, 1,000+ birds were sighted in Taylor County (B. Armbrust). Late sightings reported as follows: Forest County, May 7 (B. Reardon) and Taylor County, May 11 (B. Armbrust).

Hoary Redpoll.—Reported as follows: Price County, BOP–April 17 (M. Hardy); Shawano County, March 10–April 12 (M. Peterson); Lincoln County, March 12 (R. Hoffman); and Forest County, April 1 (D. Tessen).

Pine Siskin.—Present at beginning of period in 17 Counties, as far south as Dane, Jefferson, Milwaukee, Sauk, and Walworth Counties. A late sighting was reported in Milwaukee County, May 21 (N. Zehner). Present at the end of the period in Ashland, Door, Douglas, Price, Taylor, and Vilas Counties.

American Goldfinch.—Present during the period throughout the state.

Evening Grosbeak.—Present throughout the period in Ashland, Douglas, Price, Taylor, and Vilas Counties. Also present during the period in Barron, Door, Forest, Langlade, Marathon, Menominee, Oconto, Sawyer, and Shawano Counties.

House Sparrow.—Present during the period throughout the state.
Corrigenda—The 1991 report of a sharp-tailed sparrow in Burnett County should have been dated *May* 25, not March 25.

CONTRIBUTORS

Jim Anderson, Bill Armbrust, Philip Ashman, Jeff Baughman, Jim Baughman, Scott Baughman, Dan Belter, Murray Berner, Homer Bishop, Brian Boldt, Marilyn Bontly, David & Margaret Brasser, David Bratley, Kay Burcar, Nathan Carlsen, Kathy Castelein, David Cederstrom, Les Cowles, Jeff Dankert, Suzanne Dee, Scott Diehl, Bob Domagalski, Barbara Duerksen, Eric Epstein, Martin Evanson, Roger Everhart, Jim Frank, Alta Goff, Dennis Gustafson, Ron Gutschow, Jim Hale, Karen Hale, Ellen Hansen, Maybelle Hardy, Judy Haseleu, Jim Hoefler, Joyce Hoeft, Randy Hoffman, Allen Holzhueter, Joe Hudick, Thomas Hunter, John Idzikowski, Robbye Johnson, James Knickelbine, Dan Krysiak, Dennis Kuecherer, the Roland Kuhn Family, Steve and Patricia Kyle, David Lauten, Laura and Steven LaValley, Fred Lesher, Roy & Charlotte Lukes, K. Marken, Bob Mead, Keith Merkel, Don Nussbaum, Patricia Parsons, Ron Perala, Mark Peterson, Susan Peterson, Janine Polk, Mary Jean Raile, Rebecca Ratering, Bill Reardon, Carol Richter, Paul Risch, Sam Robbins, Carroll Rudy, Thomas Schultz, Larry Semo, Al & Sue Shea, Jerry & Karen Smith, Charles Sontag, Tom Soulen, Michael Spreeman, Gary Stout, Mark Tacke, James Toft, Daryl Tessen, Dick Verch, Mary Jo Welnak, Melvin Wierzbicki, Thomas Wood, Norma Zehner, and Tom Ziebell.

Allen K. Shea
2202 Manor Green Drive
Madison, WI 53711

Big Day Counts: 1992

by Jim Frank

The twenty-five Big Day Counts received this year is a higher than expected number of submissions. Eight of those were conducted in the southeastern part of the state, but only five were received from the usually favored northwestern part of the state. Numbers were much higher than last year with seven counts surpassing 170 species, and ten exceeding 160. For the third consecutive year, the most impressive list comes from Randy Hoffman running his northwestern corner of the state route on May 22. Inching closer to the magic 200 mark, he turned up 197 species including 29 warblers and 13 sparrows.

In total, 262 species appeared on the 25 counts (the most in the past 4 years). The most noteworthy included a Buff-breasted Sandpiper, a Loggerhead Shrike, a Little Blue Heron, a Great Black-backed Gull, Long-billed Dowitchers, and a Prairie Warbler.

Here are the details of the 25 counts; underlined species were unique to the Big Day Counts, italicized items were the largest number of that group seen on 1992 counts.

NORTHWESTERN REGION

Randy Hoffman; 5/22/92; 197 species.—The areas covered included Tamarack Creek, Trempealeau NWR, Tiffany Bottoms, Bear Creek, Meridean, Wilson Pond, Sarona Ponds, Solon Springs, Lyman Lake Bog, Wisconsin Point, and Crex Meadows.

Interesting species noted were Red-necked Grebe, American White Pelican, Trumpeter Swan, Greater Scaup Duck, Sharp-tailed Grouse, King Rail, Long-eared Owl, Tufted Titmouse, Bell's Vireo, Orange-crowned Warbler, Pine Warbler, Prothonotary Warbler, Louisiana Waterthrush, Kentucky Warbler, Connecticut Warbler, Dickcissel, Lark Sparrow, Henslow's Sparrow, Le Conte's Sparrow, *Rusty Blackbird*, Orchard Oriole, Evening Grosbeak, 2 grebes, 5 herons, *2 swans*, 14 ducks, 8 hawks, 4 galliformes, 3 rails, 15 shorebirds, 3 owls, *7 woodpeckers, 10 flycatchers,* 4 wrens, *7 thrushes, 6 vireos, 29 warblers,* 13 sparrows, and *11 blackbirds*.

Al Shea, Sue Shea; 5/27/92; 177 species.—Areas visited included Perrot St.

Table 1. Details of Big Day Counts, 1992.

Observers	Date	Area	Time	Sky	Wind	Temp	Car Miles	Foot Miles	Species
Randy Hoffman	5/22/92	NW	0:07–21:07	Clo.	S 8	67–87	412	6	197
Shea, Shea, Hoffman	5/15/92	SC	0:16–21:40	P.Cl	SW12	48–73	433	3	182
Hoffman, Shea	5/17/92	SC	3:00–19:00	Clo.	S 10	52–81	302	3	179
Baughman, Baughman, Schultz	5/17/92	SC	0:00–21:00	P.Cl	N 10	47–82	370	3	177
Shea, Shea	5/27/92	NW	2:00–10:20	P.Cl	NE10	40–65	450	3	177
Risch, Risch, Risch	5/17/92	NC	0:00–20:30	P.Cl	SW 8	48–68	382	1	173
Peterson, Anderson	5/18/92	NC	3:00–20:45	P.Cl	W 10	55–80	280	3	172
Johnson, Semo	5/26/92	NW	1:25–19:30	Fair	? 8	22–65	495	1	166
Tessen, Frank	5/16/92	SC	0:00–20:00	P.Cl	S 35	52–84	490	3	164
Frank	5/12/92	SE	3:40–20:05	Clo.	SW10	60–78	316	3	160
Shea, Shea	5/23/92	NE	1:15–20:30	Clo.	N 15	58–44	417	2	159
Hudick, Schmidt, Schaufenbuel	5/27/92	NW	4:30–21:30	P.Cl	NW 8	38–72	430	6	157
Tessen	5/29/92	NW	0:00–18:30	P.Cl	SW25	38–77	245	3	155
Burcar, Domagalski	5/16/92	SC	4:00–23:50	Fair	S 25	50–75	269	8	154
Mead, Naniot, Naniot, Berkopec, Eichhorn	5/23/92	NE	2:00–21:30	P.Cl	NE15	40–55	175	4	152
Baughman, Baughman	5/30/92	NC	3:00–21:00	P.Cl	? 5	42–76	210	3	137
Diehl	5/26/92	SE	4:30–21:20	Clo.	NE ?	38–57	252	3	136
Diehl	5/12/92	SE	5:00–19:00	Clo.	SW ?	52–70	258	2	136
Diehl	5/19/92	SE	4:30–21:00	Clo.	? 5	45–72	268	3	135
Peterson, Peterson	5/16/92	NC	3:30–20:00	Rain	SW40	55–85	?	?	134
Tessen	5/03/92	SE	6:00–18:00	P.Cl	NW20	45–56	275	2	128
Brasser, Brasser	5/16/92	SE	6:00–21:00	P.Cl	SE10	55–80	167	5	120
Tessen	5/24/92	SE	6:00–18:00	P.Cl	NE25	37–45	410	2	116
Tessen	5/02/92	SE	6:30–17:00	P.Cl	NW25	62–70	275	2	109
Tessen	5/23/92	SW	5:30–18:30	Clo.	NW20	70–55	250	3	101

Park, Tiffany Bottoms, Meridean, Wilson's Pond, Wisconsin Point, Tri-Lakes Area, Lyman Lake Bog, St. Croix Flowage, and Crex Meadows.

Interesting species included Eared Grebe, Yellow-crowned Night-Heron, Trumpeter Swan, Lesser Golden Plover, Hudsonian Godwit, Marbled Godwit, White-rumped Sandpiper, Pine Warbler, Prothonotary Warbler, Hooded Warbler, Lark Sparrow, Le Conte's Sparrow, Sharp-tailed Sparrow, Orchard Oriole, 4 herons, *2 swans*, 13 ducks, 8 hawks, 4 galliformes, 2 rails, 17 shorebirds, 2 gulls, 3 owls, *7 woodpeckers*, 7 flycatchers, 3 wrens, 5 thrushes, 4 vireos, 23 warblers, 13 sparrows, 10 blackbirds, and 5 finches.

Robbye Johnson, Larry Semo; 5/26/92; 166 species.—They birded Wisconsin Point, Stone's Bridge, Marine Landing, Willow River, Crex Mead-ows, Oak Ridge Lake, Douglas Co., St. Croix Co., and Burnett Co.

In the course of the day they encountered American White Pelican, Cattle Egret, Sharp-tailed Grouse, Lesser Golden Plover, *Buff-breasted Sandpiper*, Hudsonian Godwit, Long-eared Owl, Pine Warbler, Louisiana Waterthrush, Le Conte's Sparrow, Sharp-tailed Sparrow, Pine Siskin, Evening Grosbeak, 5 herons, 13 ducks, 8 hawks, *4 galliformes*, 16 shorebirds, 3 owls, 6 woodpeckers, 8 flycatchers, 5 thrushes, 4 vireos, 18 warblers, 10 sparrows, 9 blackbirds, and 5 finches.

Joe Hudick, Ted Schmidt, Joe Schaufenbuel; 5/27/92; 157 species.—Areas covered were Polk Co., Interstate Park, St. Croix River, St. Croix Co., Oak Ridge Lake, Crex Meadows, Fish lake, Brule River, and Wisconsin Point.

They discovered American White Pelican, Trumpeter Swan, Hudsonian

Godwit, Marbled Godwit, Pine Warbler, Louisiana Waterthrush, Prothonotary Warbler, Pine Siskin, 4 herons, *2 swans,* 10 ducks, 8 hawks, 14 shorebirds, 1 owl, 6 woodpeckers, 8 flycatchers, 4 wrens, 6 thrushes, 3 vireos, 21 warblers, 9 sparrows, and 9 blackbirds.

Daryl Tessen; 5/29/92; 155 species.—He birded Crex Meadows, Fish Lake, Solon Springs, Gordon, Stone's Bridge, Wisconsin Point, and Ashland.

Of interest were American White Pelican, Trumpeter Swan, Canvasback, *Northern Goshawk,* Merlin, Sharp-tailed Grouse, Yellow Rail, Northern Saw-whet Owl, Pine Warbler, Connecticut Warbler, Lark Sparrow, Le Conte's Sparrow, Sharp-tailed Sparrow, Pine Siskin, Evening Grosbeak, 5 herons, *2 swans,* 13 ducks, *11 hawks,* 3 rails, 10 shorebirds, 3 owls, 2 woodpeckers, 8 flycatchers, 4 thrushes, 4 vireos, 16 warblers, 12 sparrows, 9 blackbirds, and 4 finches.

NORTH CENTRAL REGION

Deborah Risch, Nick Risch, Paul Risch; 5/17/92; 173 species.—Their count covered Unity Marsh, Pershing Wildlife Area, Miller Dam Flowage, Chequamegon Nat. Forest, St. Croix Co. Ponds, Willow River, and the St. Croix River bottomlands.

Sightings included Canvasback, Sharp-tailed Grouse, Western Sandpiper, Baird's Sandpiper, *Stilt Sandpiper,* Long-eared Owl, Short-eared Owl, Northern Saw-whet Owl, Gray Jay, Tufted Titmouse, Prothonotary Warbler, Dickcissel, Lark Sparrow, Henslow's Sparrow, Le Conte's Sparrow, Pine Siskin, Evening Grosbeak, 5 herons, 12 ducks, 9 hawks, 16 shorebirds,

5 owls, 7 woodpeckers, 7 flycatchers, 4 wrens, 6 thrushes, 4 vireos, 22 warblers, 14 sparrows, 9 blackbirds, and 5 finches.

Mark Peterson, Jim Anderson; 5/18/ 92; 172 species.—Areas birded were Navarino Wildlife Area, Stockbridge Indian Reservation, Green Bay, Kewaunee, Two Rivers, Manitowoc, and Woodland Dunes.

Noteworthy birds included Cattle Egret, Tundra Swan, Greater Scaup Duck, Common Merganser, Whimbrel, Hudsonian Godwit, Western Sandpiper, Baird's Sandpiper, Orange-crowned Warbler, Black-throated Blue Warbler, Pine Warbler, Le Conte's Sparrow, Pine Siskin, Evening Grosbeak, 6 herons, 11 ducks, 8 hawks, 17 shorebirds, 2 owls, 6 woodpeckers, 6 flycatchers, 4 wrens, 7 *thrushes,* 4 vireos, 25 warblers, 12 sparrows, 9 blackbirds, and 5 finches.

Jeffrey Baughman, Jim Baughman; 5/ 30/92; 137 species.—They birded Vilas Co. including Powell Marsh, Presque Isle, Land-O-Lakes, Eagle River, Deep Lake, and Conover.

Among their sightings were Common Merganser, Northern Saw-whet Owl, Gray Jay, Pine Warbler, Connecticut Warbler, Le Conte's Sparrow, *Dark-eyed Junco,* 2 herons, 11 ducks, 7 hawks, 6 shorebirds, 5 woodpeckers, 7 flycatchers, 4 wrens, 4 thrushes, 4 vireos, 20 warblers, 10 sparrows, and 8 blackbirds.

Mark Peterson, Harold Peterson; 5/ 16/92; 134 species.—Birding only in Shawano County, they found Tundra Swan, Hudsonian Godwit, *Water Pipit,* Pine Warbler, Le Conte's Sparrow, Pine Siskin, Evening Grosbeak, 2 herons, 6 ducks, 5 hawks, 10 shorebirds, 2 owls, 6 woodpeckers, 5 flycatchers, 4 wrens, 5 thrushes, 4 vireos, 19 warblers, 11 sparrows, 9 blackbirds, and 5 finches.

NORTHEASTERN REGION

Al Shea, Sue Shea; 5/23/92; 159 species.—Areas visited included Horicon Marsh, North Kettle Moraine, Sheboygan Harbor, Manitowoc Harbor, Woodland Dunes, Green Bay's Terminal Drive, Nicolet National Forest, County A Bog, and Thunder Lake Wildlife Area.

Sightings included Canvasback, Harlequin Duck, Common Merganser, King Rail, Whimbrel, Red Knot, Franklin's Gull, Short-eared Owl, *Prairie Warbler,* Le Conte's Sparrow, 5 herons, 10 ducks, 7 hawks, 3 galliformes, 3 rails, 12 shorebirds, 4 gulls, 3 owls, 3 woodpeckers, 9 flycatchers, 4 wrens, 6 thrushes, 3 vireos, 21 warblers, 10 sparrows, and 8 blackbirds.

Bob Mead, Mark Naniot, Barb Naniot, Joan Berkopec, Ron Eichhorn; 5/23/92; 152 species.—Their day's birding took them to Peshtigo Harbor, Oconto Marsh, Barkhausen Wildlife Area, and Green Bay Wildlife Sanctuary. Their reports included Cattle Egret, Yellow Rail, White-rumped Sandpiper, Baird's Sandpiper, Franklin's Gull, *Loggerhead Shrike,* Sharptailed Sparrow, 6 herons, 10 ducks, 6 hawks, 14 shorebirds, 4 gulls, 6 woodpeckers, 8 flycatchers, 4 wrens, 5 thrushes, 3 vireos, 19 warblers, 9 sparrows, and 8 blackbirds.

SOUTHWESTERN REGION

Daryl Tessen; 5/23/92; 101 species.—Birding Roy Road, Sugar River, Yellowstone State Park, Wyalusing State Park, and Cadiz Springs State Park, he located Tufted Titmouse, *White-eyed Vireo, Yellow-throated Warbler, Worm-eating Warbler,* Kentucky Warbler, Yellow-breasted Chat, Dickcissel, Henslow's Sparrow, Orchard Oriole, 3 herons, 4 ducks, 3 hawks, 1 shorebird, 2 cuckoos, 5 woodpeckers, 4 vireos, 13 warblers, 8 sparrows, and 8 blackbirds.

SOUTH CENTRAL REGION

Al Shea, Sue Shea, Randy Hoffman; 5/15/92; 182 species.—The areas covered included Grand River Marsh, Snake Creek Wetlands, Horicon Marsh, North Kettle Moraine, Sheboygan Harbor, Lake Maria, Goose Pond, Devil's Lake, Baxter's Hollow, DM Pond, PF Prairie, and Mazomanie Bottoms.

Highlights were Red-necked Grebe, Yellow-crowned Night-Heron, Black Scoter, Peregrine Falcon, Yellow Rail, King Rail, Lesser Golden Plover, Hudsonian Godwit, Long-billed Dowitcher, Franklin's Gull, *Great Black-backed Gull,* Pine Warbler, Louisiana Waterthrush, Connecticut Warbler, Lark Sparrow, Henslow's Sparrow, Le Conte's Sparrow, Lapland Longspur, Orchard Oriole, *7 herons,* 15 ducks, 7 hawks, *4 galliformes,* 4 rails, 16 shorebirds, *5 gulls,* 3 owls, *7 woodpeckers,* 6 flycatchers, 6 thrushes, 4 vireos, 27 warblers, *14 sparrows,* and 9 blackbirds.

Randy Hoffman, Al Shea; 5/17/92; 179 species.—Areas birded included Waunakee Marsh, Mazomanie Bottoms, PF Prairie, Baxter's Hollow, Devil's Lake, Goose Pond, Lake Maria, Horicon Marsh, Breezy Point, U.W. Arboretum, University Bay, Fish

Hatchery Road Ponds, and Crystal Lake.

Birds of note were Yellow-crowned Night-Heron, Oldsquaw, Black Scoter, Peregrine Falcon, Yellow Rail, King Rail, Lesser Golden Plover, White-rumped Sandpiper, Long-billed Dowitcher, Black-throated Blue Warbler, Louisiana Waterthrush, Connecticut Warbler, Summer Tanager, Lark Sparrow, Lapland Longspur, Orchard Oriole, *7 herons,* 16 ducks, 6 hawks, *4 galliformes, 18 shorebirds,* 1 gull, 3 owls, *7 woodpeckers, 10 flycatchers,* 4 wrens, 6 thrushes, 4 vireos, 26 warblers, *2 tanagers,* 11 sparrow, and 9 blackbirds.

Jeff Baughman, Scott Baughman, Tom Schultz; 5/17/92; 177 species.—Their count covered Mud Lake Wildlife Area, Snake Creek Wetlands, Grand River Wildlife Area, Baxter's Hollow, PF Prairies, Mazomanie Bottoms, Schoeneberg Marsh, AW Ponds, Horicon Marsh, North Kettle Moraine, and Sheboygan Harbor.

Among the most interesting sightings were Canvasback, Black Scoter, Harlequin Duck, Yellow Rail, King Rail, Lesser Golden Plover, Long-eared Owl, Louisiana Waterthrush, Yellow-breasted Chat, Dickcissel, Henslow's Sparrow, Le Conte's Sparrow, Lapland Longspur, Orchard Oriole, Pine Siskin, 6 herons, 16 ducks, 7 hawks, *4 galliformes, 4 rails,* 15 shorebirds, 2 cuckoos, 3 owls, 5 woodpeckers, 8 flycatchers, 6 thrushes, 4 vireos, 24 warblers, 13 sparrows, and 9 blackbirds.

Daryl Tessen, Jim Frank; 5/16/92; 164 species.—Their Big Day stops included Cedarburg Bog, Grassy lake, Waunakee Marsh, Bert Laws Bottoms, PF Prairie, Baxter's Hollow, Crystal Lake, Picnic Point, DM Pond, Patton Pond, Goose Pond, Schoeneberg Marsh, AW Ponds, Lake Maria, Rat River Wildlife Area, Black Otter Lake, Thousand Island Wildlife Area, Atkinson Marsh, Two Rivers, Manitowoc Harbor, and Cleveland.

Interesting species were Horned Grebe, Red-necked Grebe, Canvasback, Greater Scaup Duck, Black Scoter, King Rail, Hudsonian Godwit, *Carolina Wren,* Bell's Vireo, Louisiana Waterthrush, Lark Sparrow, Orchard Oriole, *3 grebes,* 3 herons, 16 ducks, 8 hawks, 3 rails, 14 shorebirds, 3 owls, *7 woodpeckers,* 6 flycatchers, *5 wrens,* 5 thrushes, 5 vireos, 19 warblers, 11 sparrows, and 10 blackbirds.

Kay Burcar, Bob Domagalski; 5/16/92; 154 species.—Areas visited on their Big Day included Bert Laws Bottoms, Waunakee Marsh, UW Arboretum, Nine Springs Sewage Plant, Baxter's Hollow, Schlukebier Prairie, Devil's Lake, Schoeneberg Marsh, AW Ponds and Horicon NWR.

They reported Canvasback, Yellow Rail, King Rail, Lesser Golden Plover, Hudsonian Godwit, White-rumped Sandpiper, Summer Tanager, 5 herons, 8 ducks, 4 hawks, *4 rails,* 17 shorebirds, 2 cuckoos, 3 owls, 6 woodpeckers, 8 flycatchers, 6 thrushes, 4 vireos, 24 warblers, *2 tanagers,* 11 sparrows, and 8 blackbirds.

SOUTHEASTERN REGION

Jim Frank; 5/12/92; 160 species.—His day began at Cedarburg Bog and included stops at Kletzsch Park, Lincoln Park, Estabrook Park, Schlitz Audubon Center, Virmond Park, Concordia College, Ulao Parkway, Port Washington Harbor, Belgium

Pond, Horicon NWR, AW Ponds, Manitowoc Harbor, and Two Rivers.

Some of the birds seen were Canvasback, Greater Scaup Duck, Peregrine Falcon, Lesser Golden Plover, Black-throated Blue Warbler, Orchard Oriole, 5 herons, 15 ducks, 7 hawks, 14 shorebirds, 2 owls, 5 woodpeckers, 7 flycatchers, 4 wrens, 6 thrushes, 3 vireos, 23 warblers, 11 sparrows, and 9 blackbirds.

Scott Diehl; 5/26/92; 136 species.—Areas covered were Cedarburg Bog, Riveredge Nature Center, Belgium Pond, Harrington Beach State Park, Ehler's Park, Covered Bridge Park, Horicon NWR, Theresa Marsh, AW Ponds, Milwaukee Coast Guard Impoundment, Phantom Lake, and Vernon Marsh.

His list included Cattle Egret, Peregrine Falcon, Marbled Godwit, Pine Warbler, Le Conte's Sparrow, 5 herons, 10 ducks, 5 hawks, 9 shorebirds, 2 owls, 5 woodpeckers, 8 flycatchers, 5 thrushes, 3 vireos, 14 warblers, 10 sparrows, and 8 blackbirds.

Scott Diehl; 5/12/92; 136 species.—On this Big Day, he visited Cedarburg Bog, Riveredge Nature Center, Milwaukee Coast Guard Impoundment, Theresa Marsh, Horicon Marsh, Belgium Pond, Harrington Beach State Park, Virmond Park, and Whitnall Park to find Canvasback, 5 herons, 12 ducks, 4 hawks, 7 shorebirds, 1 owl, 4 woodpeckers, 7 flycatchers, 6 thrushes, 2 vireos, 20 warblers, 11 sparrows, and 8 blackbirds.

Scott Diehl; 5/19/92; 135 species.—Once again he birded Cedarburg Bog, Riveredge Nature Center, Belgium Pond, Harrington Beach State Park,

Horicon NWR, Theresa Marsh, Milwaukee Coast Guard Impoundment, Phantom Lake, Wind Lake Sod Farm, and Vernon Marsh.

Sightings included King Rail, Pine Warbler, 5 herons, 10 ducks, 5 hawks, 3 rails, 8 shorebirds, 1 owl, 4 woodpeckers, 8 flycatchers, 4 thrushes, 5 vireos, 20 warblers, 10 sparrows, and 8 blackbirds.

Daryl Tessen; 5/3/92; 128 species.—This Big Day covered Duck Lake Walkway, Milwaukee Coast Guard Impoundment, Estabrook Park, Kletzsch Park, Virmond Park, Harrington Beach State Park, Belgium Pond, Theresa Marsh, KK Pond, Horicon NWR, Breezy Point Road, AW Ponds, and Oconomowoc,

The best birds were Horned Grebe, Greater Scaup Duck, Oldsquaw, Surf Scoter, *Common Goldeneye*, White-rumped Sandpiper, Long-billed Dowitcher, Black-throated Blue Warbler, Louisiana Waterthrush, Henslow's Sparrow, 2 herons, *19 ducks,* 5 hawks, 12 shorebirds, 2 owls, 3 woodpeckers, 2 flycatchers, 7 thrushes, 1 vireo, 18 warblers, 8 sparrows, and 7 blackbirds.

David Brasser, Margaret Brasser; 5/16/92; 120 species.—They traveled to Horicon NWR, Theresa Marsh, Riveredge Nature Center, Belgium Pond, Harrington Beach State Park, Terry Andrae State Park, Sheboygan Harbor, and Maywood Environmental Center to tally *Little Blue Heron,* Canvasback, Merlin, *6 herons,* 10 ducks, 5 hawks, 5 shorebirds, 2 woodpeckers, 5 flycatchers, 4 vireos, 17 warblers, 7 sparrows, and 7 blackbirds.

Daryl Tessen; 5/24/92; 116 species.—A trip to Mukwonago, Vernon Marsh,

Lapham Peak, Milwaukee Coast Guard Impoundment, Estabrook Park, Harrington Beach State Park, Sheboygan Harbor, Manitowoc Harbor, Two Rivers, Horicon Marsh, AW Ponds, and Scuppernong Marsh yielded a *Snow Goose,* Harlequin Duck, Peregrine Falcon, Hudsonian Godwit, Red Knot, White-rumped Sandpiper, Baird's Sandpiper, Connecticut Warbler, Hooded Warbler, 10 ducks, 5 hawks, 12 shorebirds, 5 flycatchers, 5 thrushes, 3 vireos, 17 warblers, 6 sparrows, and 9 blackbirds.

Daryl Tessen; 5/2/92; 109 species.— This early May Big Day covered Fontana, Darien Park, Natureland Park, Storr's Wildlife Area, Grass Lake, Fulton, Blarney Pond, Swan Pond, DM Pond, Patton Pond, Goose Pond, Schoeneberg Marsh, Mud Lake Wildlife Area, Jamison Park, and Lake Wisconsin.

Birds of note were *Gray Partridge,* Orange-crowned Warbler, *Harris' Sparrow,* Lapland Longspur, 2 herons, 11 ducks, 3 hawks, 7 shorebirds, 5 flycatchers, 2 vireos, 13 warblers, 10 sparrows, and 8 blackbirds.

Jim Frank
4339 West Laverna Ave.
Mequon, WI 53092

Scissor-tailed Flycatcher *by Frank Mittelstadt.*

May Day Counts: 1992

by Jim Frank

The 24 May Day Counts conducted this year represent an average number of counts over the past ten years. Leading the list for participation were Racine/Kenosha (26), Waukesha (24), Winnebago (23) and Oxbo/Fifield (22). Total species reported were back to average this year after a dip in 1991. Six counts exceeded 150 species with Winnebago once again leading the way with an impressive 177 species on May 9th, in spite of a slow to materialize migration. Racine/Kenosha reported a list of 165 species. The other counts with lists greater than 150 species were Marathon, Ashland/Bayfield, Shawano, and Fond du Lac.

This years 245 species compares to 245 in 1989, 244 in 1990, and 242 in 1991. Most species of hawks and owls were reported with greater frequency this year for uncertain reasons. The increased reports of Northern Waterthrush, Parula, Palm, and Nashville Warblers are probably a reflection of the delayed migration this spring. These species are usually past peak migration by the dates of most May Counts. Increased White-throated and White-crowned Sparrows may also re-

flect the slow spring. To no one's surprise, House Finches continue to increase in frequency, only eluding the northernmost counts. The most distressing report or lack of reporting is the total absence of Yellow-billed Cuckoos on all 24 of the May Counts.

The most interesting sightings include a Cinnamon Teal from Lake Mills, a Piping Plover from Racine/Kenosha, a Red-necked Phalarope from Winnebago County, a Black-backed Woodpecker from Taylor County, a Boreal Chickadee from Vilas County, a Loggerhead Shrike from Oconto County, and last, but certainly not least—a Western Tanager from Fond du Lac County.

Mention should also be made of the 4 counts that completed their May Counts on May 9th, submitting numbers of each species for inclusion in the North American Migration Count. These were Winnebago, Buffalo, Kenosha, and Ozaukee Counties. Though it is apparent the majority of Wisconsin birders do not wish to participate in this study, those that want to continue to compile such data will find it submitted to the national data bank. If enough information is gathered, a more complete discussion may occur in these pages.

Table 1. Details of the counts.

Name of Count	Date	Time	Sky	Wind	Temp	Observers	Parties	Species
Ashland/Bayfield	5/20	04:00–17:00	Clear	SW 8	56–88	16	4	151
Burnett	5/18	04:26–21:10	Clear	S 10	38–70	3	2	134
Buffalo	5/09	04:40–19:30	Clear	? 0	48–71	4	2	88
Oxbo/Fifield	5/16	09:00–21:00	Clo.	SW 5	52–74	22	15	123
Taylor	5/16	04:30–20:30	P.Cl.	SE15	57–73	5	3	112
Marathon	5/16	04:00–14:00	P.Cl.	S 30	46–69	17	14	152
Portage	5/09	04:45–17:00	Clear	S 5	48–78	12	?	131
Shawano	5/16	03:30–20:00	P.Cl.	SW30	55–85	12	9	151
Oconto	5/16	01:30–19:00	Clo.	S 20	49–77	2	1	149
Vilas	5/30	03:00–21:00	P.Cl.	NE 6	42–76	2	1	137
Calumet	5/09	05:00–20:00	Clear	E 5	45–75	10	6	116
Winnebago	5/09	04:45–22:00	Clear	E 7	48–78	23	14	177
Fond du Lac	5/16	05:00–20:30	P.Cl.	S 10	52–76	18	7	152
Shiocton	5/16	06:30–15:00	Clear	S 8	55–81	8	2	90
Horicon	5/16	05:00–20:00	Clear	? 0	40–65	14	9	144
Ozaukee	5/09	03:30–15:00	P.Cl.	NE 8	48–66	3	1	102
Racine/Kenosha	5/16	03:30–21:00	P.Cl.	S 10	60–78	26	18	165
Plymouth	5/16	05:30–17:00	P.Cl.	SE 8	47–60	13	6	135
Waukesha	5/16	05:00–17:00	P.Cl.	SE ?	56–80	24	8	135
Oconomowoc	5/10	04:00–19:00	Clear	SW 5	61–80	15	7	138
Lake Geneva	5/09	04:00–20:00	Clear	SW 6	44–80	5	2	101
Lake Mills	5/14	05:30–18:40	Clo.	E 8	44–65	2	1	95
Rock	5/09	?	Clear	S 5	?-70	?	?	78
Kenosha	5/09	04:00–20:00	Clear	NE 6	50–78	2	2	127

Table 2. Species found on 5 or more counts in northern Wisconsin.

Species	Ashland/Bayfield	Burnett Co.	Buffalo Co.	Oxbo/Fifield	Taylor Co.	Marathon Co.	Portage Co.	Shawano Co.	Oconto Co.	Vilas Co.	# of Counts 1992	# of Counts 1991	# of Counts 1990	# of Counts 1989
Common Loon	X	X	—	X	X	X	—	—	X	X	9	5	8	11
Pied-billed Grebe	—	X	X	—	X	X	X	X	X	X	20	13	16	15
Double-crested Cormorant	X	X	X	—	X	X	X	—	X	—	12	12	8	11
American Bittern	X	X	—	X	X	X	X	X	X	X	17	13	15	16
Least Bittern	—	—	—	—	—	X	—	—	X	—	5	4	4	3
Great Blue Heron	X	X	X	X	X	X	X	X	X	X	24	21	22	22
Great Egret	—	—	X	—	X	X	—	—	—	—	10	7	10	11
Green-backed Heron	X	—	X	X	X	X	X	X	X	—	20	21	19	21
Black-crowned Night-Heron	—	—	—	—	—	X	—	—	X	—	6	7	8	8
Mute Swan	X	—	—	—	—	—	X	—	—	—	5	3	4	7
Canada Goose	X	X	X	—	X	X	X	X	X	X	22	20	21	19
Wood Duck	X	X	X	X	X	X	X	X	X	X	24	20	22	21
Green-winged Teal	X	X	—	—	—	X	X	X	X	X	13	10	11	10
American Black Duck	X	X	—	—	X	X	—	—	—	X	9	7	6	5
Mallard	X	X	X	X	X	X	X	X	X	X	24	22	21	22
Northern Pintail	—	—	—	—	—	—	X	—	X	—	7	6	5	0

(continued)

Table 2. *Continued*

Species	Ashland/Bayfield	Burnett Co.	Buffalo Co.	Oxbo/Fifield	Taylor Co.	Marathon Co.	Portage Co.	Shawano Co.	Oconto Co.	Vilas Co.	# of Counts 1992	# of Counts 1991	# of Counts 1990	# of Counts 1989
Blue-winged Teal	X	X	X	—	X	X	X	X	X	X	23	21	22	20
Northern Shoveler	—	—	—	—	—	—	X	X	—	X	14	14	14	10
Gadwall	X	X	—	—	—	—	—	—	—	X	8	4	7	9
American Wigeon	X	X	—	X	—	—	—	—	—	—	6	8	8	11
Canvasback	X	X	—	—	—	—	—	—	—	—	5	1	4	3
Redhead	—	—	—	—	—	—	—	—	—	—	7	5	5	9
Ring-necked Duck	—	X	—	—	X	X	—	X	—	X	10	7	8	9
Greater Scaup Duck	X	—	—	—	X	—	—	—	—	—	6	1	2	1
Lesser Scaup Duck	X	—	—	X	—	—	X	—	—	X	9	9	12	8
Common Goldeneye	X	—	—	X	—	—	—	X	—	—	5	1	3	5
Bufflehead	X	—	—	X	—	X	—	—	—	—	5	3	7	6
Hooded Merganser	X	X	—	X	—	X	X	X	—	X	9	7	7	8
Common Merganser	X	—	—	X	—	—	—	—	—	X	5	4	3	4
Ruddy Duck	—	—	—	—	—	X	X	—	—	—	9	7	10	10
Turkey Vulture	—	X	X	—	—	—	X	X	X	X	19	15	11	16
Osprey	—	X	—	X	—	X	X	X	X	X	13	8	7	11
Bald Eagle	X	X	—	X	X	X	·X	X	X	X	10	8	7	5
Northern Harrier	X	X	—	X	X	X	X	—	X	X	18	12	15	14
Sharp-shinned Hawk	X	X	—	X	X	X	—	—	X	X	17	7	9	10
Cooper's Hawk	—	X	X	—	—	X	X	—	X	—	9	7	9	12
Red-shouldered Hawk	—	X	—	X	—	—	X	—	—	—	5	5	5	5
Broad-winged Hawk	X	X	X	X	X	X	X	X	X	X	18	11	11	13
Red-tailed Hawk	X	X	X	X	X	X	X	X	X	X	24	21	20	21
American Kestrel	X	X	X	X	X	X	X	X	X	X	24	22	21	21
Ring-necked Pheasant	—	—	—	—	X	X	—	X	—	—	13	13	15	13
Ruffed Grouse	X	X	X	X	X	X	X	X	X	X	14	14	14	16
Wild Turkey	—	X	X	—	—	—	—	—	—	—	7	5	4	3
Virginia Rail	—	—	—	—	X	—	—	—	X	X	8	5	7	8
Sora	X	X	—	X	X	X	X	X	X	X	23	15	20	15
American Coot	—	X	—	—	—	X	—	X	—	—	16	13	17	15
Sandhill Crane	X	X	X	X	X	X	X	X	X	X	23	18	18	18
Semipalmated Plover	X	X	—	—	—	—	X	X	X	—	13	7	6	11
Killdeer	X	X	X	X	X	X	X	X	X	X	24	21	21	21
Greater Yellowlegs	X	X	—	—	—	X	X	X	—	—	13	8	13	10
Lesser Yellowlegs	X	X	—	—	—	X	—	X	—	—	12	7	14	13
Solitary Sandpiper	X	—	—	X	—	X	X	—	—	—	10	10	13	9
Spotted Sandpiper	X	X	X	X	X	X	X	X	X	X	21	18	18	19
Upland Sandpiper	—	X	—	—	X	—	—	X	—	—	6	6	6	8
Semipalmated Sandpiper	X	X	—	—	—	—	—	—	X	X	9	6	6	8
Least Sandpiper	X	X	—	—	—	X	X	X	X	X	16	9	12	13
Pectoral Sandpiper	X	—	—	—	—	—	—	—	X	—	9	6	4	9
Dunlin	X	X	—	—	—	—	—	—	—	X	9	9	4	8
Short-billed Dowitcher	X	—	—	—	—	—	—	X	—	—	8	6	5	6
Common Snipe	X	X	—	X	X	X	X	X	X	X	18	15	19	17
American Woodcock	X	X	—	X	X	X	—	X	X	—	17	10	18	11
Bonaparte's Gull	X	X	—	—	—	—	—	—	—	—	8	7	7	7
Ring-billed Gull	X	—	—	X	X	X	X	X	X	—	17	19	14	14
Herring Gull	X	—	X	—	—	—	—	—	X	—	9	7	9	10
Caspian Tern	X	—	—	—	—	—	—	—	X	—	6	5	7	7
Common Tern	X	X	—	—	—	—	—	—	X	—	9	7	10	10
Forster's Tern	—	—	—	—	—	—	—	X	X	—	9	10	14	7
Black Tern	X	X	—	—	—	X	X	X	X	X	19	16	16	17
Rock Dove	X	X	X	X	X	X	X	X	X	—	23	22	21	22
Mourning Dove	X	X	X	X	X	X	X	X	X	X	24	22	22	23
Black-billed Cuckoo	—	X	X	—	—	X	—	X	X	X	11	10	8	14
Great Horned Owl	X	X	X	—	X	X	X	X	X	X	19	11	16	15
Barred Owl	—	X	—	X	X	X	X	X	X	—	14	6	12	10
Common Nighthawk	X	X	—	—	—	X	—	—	—	X	9	13	9	16
Whip-poor-will	—	X	—	X	—	X	—	—	—	X	7	8	8	12
Chimney Swift	X	X	X	—	X	X	X	X	X	X	22	20	20	22
Ruby-throated Hummingbird	X	X	—	X	X	X	—	X	X	X	16	15	13	14
Belted Kingfisher	X	—	X	X	X	X	X	X	X	X	23	17	18	21
Red-headed Woodpecker	—	X	X	X	X	X	X	X	X	—	20	17	19	21

(*continued*)

Table 2. *Continued*

Species	Ashland/Bayfield	Burnett Co.	Buffalo Co.	Oxbo/Fifield	Taylor Co.	Marathon Co.	Portage Co.	Shawano Co.	Oconto Co.	Vilas Co.	# of Counts 1992	# of Counts 1991	# of Counts 1990	# of Counts 1989
Red-bellied Woodpecker	—	X	X	—	—	X	X	X	X	—	19	16	17	20
Yellow-bellied Sapsucker	X	X	X	X	X	X	X	X	X	X	11	8	10	10
Downy Woodpecker	—	X	X	X	X	X	X	X	X	X	23	22	21	23
Hairy Woodpecker	X	X	X	X	X	X	X	X	X	X	22	19	21	21
Northern Flicker	X	X	X	X	X	X	X	X	X	X	24	22	22	22
Pileated Woodpecker	X	X	—	X	X	X	X	X	—	X	11	9	10	9
Eastern Wood Pewee	—	X	—	—	X	X	—	X	X	X	10	13	13	16
Least Flycatcher	X	X	X	X	X	X	X	X	X	X	21	18	20	19
Eastern Phoebe	X	X	X	X	X	X	X	X	X	X	23	19	20	19
Great Crested Flycatcher	X	X	X	X	X	X	X	X	X	X	24	20	21	21
Eastern Kingbird	X	X	X	X	X	X	X	X	X	X	23	22	21	21
Horned Lark	X	X	X	—	—	X	X	X	X	X	21	17	18	19
Purple Martin	X	X	X	X	X	X	X	X	X	X	23	19	19	21
Tree Swallow	X	X	X	X	X	X	X	X	X	X	24	22	22	21
Northern Rough-winged Swallow	X	X	X	X	X	X	X	X	X	X	24	17	20	21
Bank Swallow	X	—	X	—	X	X	—	X	X	X	20	16	14	16
Cliff Swallow	X	X	—	X	X	X	X	X	X	X	16	13	16	16
Barn Swallow	X	X	X	X	X	X	X	X	X	X	24	22	21	22
Blue Jay	X	X	X	X	X	X	X	X	X	X	24	22	22	23
American Crow	X	X	X	X	X	X	X	X	X	X	24	22	22	23
Common Raven	X	X	—	X	X	—	X	X	X	X	8	8	5	8
Black-capped Chickadee	X	X	X	X	X	X	X	X	X	X	24	22	22	23
Red-breasted Nuthatch	X	—	—	X	X	X	X	X	X	X	12	7	15	10
White-breasted Nuthatch	X	X	X	X	X	X	X	X	X	X	22	24	21	23
Brown Creeper	—	—	—	X	—	—	X	X	—	X	8	6	0	13
House Wren	X	X	X	X	X	X	X	X	X	X	24	22	21	23
Winter Wren	X	X	—	X	—	X	X	X	X	X	10	7	5	9
Sedge Wren	X	X	—	X	X	X	X	X	X	X	17	13	16	10
Marsh Wren	X	X	—	—	—	X	X	X	X	X	16	11	14	7
Ruby-crowned Kinglet	—	—	—	X	—	X	X	X	—	X	15	7	14	15
Blue-gray Gnatcatcher	—	—	X	—	—	X	X	—	X	—	15	14	14	15
Eastern Bluebird	X	X	X	X	X	X	X	X	X	X	24	21	22	21
Veery	X	X	—	X	X	X	—	X	X	X	18	15	20	17
Gray-cheeked Thrush	—	—	—	—	—	X	—	X	—	—	8	7	10	4
Swainson's Thrush	—	—	—	X	X	X	X	—	X	—	14	13	14	11
Hermit Thrush	X	X	—	X	X	X	—	X	X	X	14	10	12	13
Wood Thrush	X	—	X	X	X	X	X	X	X	—	21	19	19	19
American Robin	X	X	X	X	X	X	X	X	X	X	24	22	22	23
Gray Catbird	X	X	X	X	X	X	X	X	X	—	23	22	21	23
Brown Thrasher	X	X	X	X	X	X	X	X	X	—	23	21	20	21
Cedar Waxwing	X	—	X	—	X	X	X	X	—	—	16	14	13	15
European Starling	X	X	X	X	X	X	X	X	X	—	23	22	22	23
Solitary Vireo	X	—	X	—	—	—	X	X	—	X	9	6	9	9
Yellow-throated Vireo	—	X	X	—	—	X	—	X	X	X	13	14	12	16
Warbling Vireo	X	X	X	X	X	X	X	X	X	X	22	20	19	16
Red-eyed Vireo	X	X	—	X	X	X	X	X	X	X	19	21	17	19
Blue-winged Warbler	—	—	X	—	—	—	X	X	—	—	11	12	13	10
Golden-winged Warbler	—	X	X	X	X	X	X	X	X	—	14	9	13	16
Tennessee Warbler	X	X	X	—	—	X	X	X	X	—	18	16	15	17
Nashville Warbler	X	X	—	X	—	X	X	X	X	X	20	16	18	18
Northern Parula Warbler	X	—	X	X	—	—	—	—	—	X	12	4	9	10
Yellow Warbler	X	X	X	X	X	X	X	X	X	X	24	20	21	22
Chestnut-sided Warbler	X	X	—	X	X	X	X	X	X	X	20	18	17	18
Magnolia Warbler	X	—	—	X	—	X	—	X	X	X	17	16	19	16
Cape May Warbler	X	—	—	—	X	—	X	X	—	14	12	10	13
Black-throated Blue Warbler	X	—	—	—	X	X	—	—	—	X	7	4	2	7
Yellow-rumped Warbler	X	X	X	X	X	X	X	X	X	X	22	18	22	20
Black-throated Green Warbler	X	—	—	—	X	X	X	X	X	X	19	16	17	18
Blackburnian Warbler	X	—	X	X	—	X	—	X	X	X	19	14	16	13
Pine Warbler	—	—	—	—	X	X	X	X	X	X	6	8	6	9
Palm Warbler	X	—	X	X	X	X	X	X	X	X	22	12	19	17
Bay-breasted Warbler	X	—	—	—	X	—	—	X	X	13	12	13	14
Blackpoll Warbler	—	—	—	X	—	X	—	—	—	—	9	14	10	11

(continued)

Table 2. *Continued*

Species	Ashland/Bayfield	Burnett Co.	Buffalo Co.	Oxbo/Fifield	Taylor Co.	Marathon Co.	Portage Co.	Shawano Co.	Oconto Co.	Vilas Co.	# of Counts 1992	# of Counts 1991	# of Counts 1990	# of Counts 1989
Cerulean Warbler	—	—	—	—	—	—	—	—	X	—	7	7	3	8
Black-and-White Warbler	X	X	—	X	—	X	X	X	X	X	19	16	20	21
American Redstart	X	X	X	X	X	X	X	X	X	X	21	18	19	20
Ovenbird	X	X	X	X	—	X	X	X	X	X	22	19	20	21
Northern Waterthrush	X	X	X	X	—	X	X	X	X	X	19	11	16	12
Connecticut Warbler	X	—	—	—	—	X	—	—	—	X	6	5	3	2
Mourning Warbler	X	—	—	X	—	X	—	—	X	X	8	11	8	11
Common Yellowthroat	X	X	X	X	X	X	X	X	X	X	24	20	21	22
Wilson's Warbler	X	X	—	—	X	X	—	X	X	—	14	10	15	12
Canada Warbler	X	X	—	—	X	X	—	X	X	X	14	13	7	9
Scarlet Tanager	—	X	—	X	—	X	—	X	—	X	17	17	16	17
Northern Cardinal	X	X	X	X	X	X	X	X	X	—	23	20	20	22
Rose-breasted Grosbeak	X	X	X	X	X	X	X	X	X	X	24	22	22	23
Indigo Bunting	X	X	—	X	X	X	—	X	X	X	20	20	18	19
Rufous-sided Towhee	X	X	—	—	—	X	X	X	X	X	19	18	18	17
Chipping Sparrow	X	X	X	X	X	X	X	X	X	X	24	22	22	21
Clay-colored Sparrow	X	X	X	X	X	X	X	X	X	X	12	11	10	12
Field Sparrow	—	X	—	X	—	X	X	X	X	—	18	17	18	19
Vesper Sparrow	X	X	X	X	—	X	X	X	X	X	17	15	16	15
Savannah Sparrow	X	X	X	—	X	X	X	X	—	X	21	19	21	19
Grasshopper Sparrow	—	—	—	—	—	X	X	X	—	—	9	8	6	7
Henslow's Sparrow	—	—	—	—	—	—	—	—	—	—	5	1	3	4
Le Conte's Sparrow	—	X	—	X	—	—	X	—	—	X	5	4	4	2
Song Sparrow	X	X	X	X	X	X	X	X	X	X	24	22	20	23
Lincoln's Sparrow	—	—	—	X	—	—	X	—	X	X	12	5	5	12
Swamp Sparrow	X	X	X	X	X	X	X	X	X	X	21	19	20	19
White-throated Sparrow	X	—	X	X	X	X	X	X	X	X	23	15	21	18
White-crowned Sparrow	X	—	X	X	X	X	X	X	X	—	21	13	19	15
Dark-eyed Junco	—	—	—	X	—	—	—	X	—	X	5	3	6	7
Bobolink	X	X	X	X	X	X	X	X	X	X	22	20	19	19
Red-winged Blackbird	X	X	X	X	X	X	X	X	X	X	24	22	22	23
Eastern Meadowlark	X	X	X	—	X	X	X	X	X	—	22	22	19	18
Western Meadowlark	X	X	—	—	X	X	X	X	X	X	15	11	16	12
Yellow-headed Blackbird	X	X	—	X	—	X	X	X	X	X	19	15	16	17
Brewer's Blackbird	X	X	—	X	X	X	X	X	X	X	14	12	14	16
Common Grackle	X	X	X	X	X	X	X	X	X	X	24	22	21	23
Brown-headed Cowbird	X	X	X	X	X	X	X	X	X	X	24	22	21	23
Northern Oriole	X	X	X	X	X	X	X	X	X	X	24	22	21	22
Purple Finch	X	—	—	X	X	X	X	X	X	X	17	13	13	9
House Finch	—	—	—	—	X	X	X	X	X	—	19	16	12	11
Pine Siskin	X	—	—	X	X	X	X	X	X	—	10	6	18	4
American Goldfinch	X	X	X	X	X	X	X	X	X	X	24	22	22	23
Evening Grosbeak	X	—	—	X	X	—	X	X	X	X	7	3	4	4
House Sparrow	X	X	X	X	X	X	X	X	X	X	24	21	22	23

Table 3. Species found on 5 or more counts in southern Wisconsin.

Species	Calumet Co.	Winnebago Co.	Fond du Lac Co.	Shiocton	Horicon	Ozaukee Co.	Racine/Kenosha	Plymouth	Waukesha Co.	Oconomowoc	Lake Geneva	Lake Mills	Rock Co.	Kenosha Co.
Common Loon	—	X	—	—	—	X	—	—	—	—	—	—	—	—
Pied-billed Grebe	X	X	X	—	X	—	X	X	X	X	X	X	—	X
Double-crested Cormorant	—	X	—	X	X	X	—	—	—	—	—	—	—	X
American Bittern	X	X	X	—	X	X	X	—	—	X	—	—	—	X
Least Bittern	—	X	X	—	X	—	—	—	—	—	—	—	—	—

(continued)

Table 3. *Continued*

Species	Calumet Co.	Winnebago Co.	Fond du Lac Co.	Shiocton	Horicon	Ozaukee Co.	Racine/Kenosha	Plymouth	Waukesha Co.	Oconomowoc	Lake Geneva	Lake Mills	Rock Co.	Kenosha Co.
Great Blue Heron	X	X	X	X	X	X	X	X	X	X	X	X	X	X
Great Egret	—	X	X	X	X	—	X	—	—	X	—	X	X	X
Green-backed Heron	X	X	X	—	X	—	X	X	X	X	X	X	X	X
Black-crowned Night-Heron	—	X	X	—	X	—	X	—	—	—	—	—	—	—
Mute Swan	—	—	—	—	—	—	X	—	—	X	X	—	—	—
Canada Goose	X	X	X	X	X	X	—	X	X	X	X	X	X	X
Wood Duck	X	X	X	X	X	X	X	X	X	X	X	X	X	X
Green-winged Teal	X	X	X	—	X	—	X	—	—	X	—	—	—	—
American Black Duck	—	X	—	—	X	—	—	—	—	X	—	—	—	X
Mallard	X	X	X	X	X	X	X	X	X	X	X	X	X	X
Northern Pintail	X	X	—	—	X	—	—	—	—	X	—	—	—	X
Blue-winged Teal	X	X	X	X	X	X	X	X	X	X	X	X	X	X
Northern Shoveler	—	X	X	—	X	X	X	X	X	X	X	—	X	X
Gadwall	—	X	X	—	X	X	X	X	—	—	—	—	—	—
American Wigeon	—	X	—	—	—	—	X	—	—	—	—	—	X	—
Canvasback	—	X	—	—	X	—	—	—	—	—	—	—	—	X
Redhead	X	X	X	—	X	—	X	—	—	—	—	—	X	X
Ring-necked Duck	—	X	—	—	X	X	—	—	—	X	—	—	—	X
Greater Scaup Duck	—	X	—	—	—	X	—	X	—	—	—	—	—	X
Lesser Scaup Duck	X	X	—	—	X	—	X	—	—	—	—	—	X	—
Common Goldeneye	—	X	—	—	—	—	—	—	—	—	—	—	—	X
Bufflehead	—	X	—	—	—	X	—	—	—	—	—	—	—	—
Hooded Merganser	—	X	—	X	—	—	—	—	—	—	—	—	—	—
Common Merganser	—	X	—	—	—	—	—	—	—	—	—	—	—	X
Ruddy Duck	—	X	X	—	X	—	—	—	X	X	X	—	—	X
Turkey Vulture	X	X	X	—	X	X	X	X	X	X	X	X	X	X
Osprey	—	X	X	—	—	—	X	X	X	—	—	—	X	—
Bald Eagle	—	—	—	—	—	—	—	—	—	—	—	—	—	X
Northern Harrier	X	X	X	—	X	—	X	X	X	X	—	—	X	X
Sharp-shinned Hawk	X	X	X	—	X	—	X	X	X	X	X	—	—	X
Cooper's Hawk	—	X	—	—	—	X	—	—	X	—	X	X	—	—
Red-shouldered Hawk	—	—	X	—	—	—	—	X	—	—	—	—	—	—
Broad-winged Hawk	—	—	X	—	—	X	X	X	X	X	X	—	—	—
Red-tailed Hawk	X	X	X	X	X	X	X	X	X	X	X	X	X	X
American Kestrel	X	X	X	X	X	X	X	X	X	X	X	X	X	X
Ring-necked Pheasant	—	X	X	—	X	—	X	—	X	X	X	X	—	X
Ruffed Grouse	X	X	X	—	—	—	—	—	X	—	—	—	—	—
Wild Turkey	X	X	—	—	—	—	—	X	X	X	—	—	—	—
Virginia Rail	X	X	X	—	—	X	—	—	—	X	—	—	—	—
Sora	X	X	X	X	X	X	X	X	X	X	X	X	X	X
American Coot	X	X	X	—	X	—	X	X	X	X	X	X	X	X
Sandhill Crane	X	X	X	—	X	X	X	X	X	X	X	X	X	X
Semipalmated Plover	X	X	X	—	X	—	X	—	X	X	—	X	—	—
Killdeer	X	X	X	X	X	X	X	X	X	X	X	X	X	X
Greater Yellowlegs	X	X	X	—	X	—	X	—	X	X	X	—	X	—
Lesser Yellowlegs	X	X	—	X	X	X	X	—	X	—	X	—	—	—
Solitary Sandpiper	X	X	—	—	X	—	X	—	X	X	—	—	—	X
Spotted Sandpiper	X	X	X	—	X	X	X	X	X	X	X	—	—	X
Upland Sandpiper	—	X	—	—	—	—	X	X	—	—	—	—	—	—
Semipalmated Sandpiper	X	X	—	—	—	—	X	—	X	X	—	—	—	—
Least Sandpiper	X	X	—	—	X	—	X	X	X	X	—	—	—	—
Pectoral Sandpiper	X	X	—	—	X	—	—	—	X	—	—	—	—	—
Dunlin	X	X	X	—	X	—	X	—	X	—	—	—	—	—
Short-billed Dowitcher	—	X	X	—	X	—	X	—	X	—	—	X	—	—
Common Snipe	X	X	X	—	X	—	X	X	—	X	X	—	—	X
American Woodcock	X	X	X	—	X	X	X	X	X	X	—	—	—	X
Bonaparte's Gull	—	X	—	—	X	X	X	X	—	—	—	—	—	X
Ring-billed Gull	X	X	X	X	X	X	X	X	X	—	—	—	—	X
Herring Gull	—	X	—	—	X	—	X	X	X	—	—	—	—	X
Caspian Tern	—	X	—	—	X	—	X	X	X	—	—	—	—	X
Common Tern	—	X	—	—	X	X	X	X	—	—	—	—	—	X
Forster's Tern	—	X	X	—	X	X	X	X	—	—	—	—	—	X
Black Tern	X	X	X	X	X	—	X	X	X	X	X	—	X	X
Rock Dove	X	X	X	X	X	X	X	X	X	X	X	X	X	X
Mourning Dove	X	X	X	X	X	X	X	X	X	X	X	X	X	X

(continued)

Table 3. *Continued*

Species	Calumet Co.	Winnebago Co.	Fond du Lac Co.	Shiocton	Horicon	Ozaukee Co.	Racine/Kenosha	Plymouth	Waukesha Co.	Oconomowoc	Lake Geneva	Lake Mills	Rock Co.	Kenosha Co.
Black-billed Cuckoo	−	−	X	−	−	−	X	−	X	X	−	X	−	−
Great Horned Owl	X	X	X	−	X	X	X	X	−	X	X	−	−	X
Barred Owl	X	−	X	X	−	X	−	X	−	X	X	X	−	−
Common Nighthawk	−	X	X	−	−	−	X	−	X	−	X	−	−	−
Whip-poor-will	−	−	−	−	−	−	−	−	−	X	−	−	−	−
Chimney Swift	X	X	X	X	X	X	X	X	X	X	X	X	−	X
Ruby-throated Hummingbird	−	X	X	X	−	−	X	X	X	X	X	−	−	−
Belted Kingfisher	X	X	X	X	X	X	X	X	X	X	X	X	X	X
Red-headed Woodpecker	X	X	−	X	X	X	X	X	X	X	X	−	X	X
Red-bellied Woodpecker	X	X	X	X	X	X	X	X	X	X	X	X	X	X
Yellow-bellied Sapsucker	−	−	−	−	−	−	−	−	−	−	−	−	−	X
Downy Woodpecker	X	X	X	X	X	X	X	X	X	X	X	X	X	X
Hairy Woodpecker	X	X	X	X	X	−	X	X	X	X	X	X	X	−
Northern Flicker	X	X	X	X	X	X	X	X	X	X	X	X	X	X
Pileated Woodpecker	−	−	X	−	−	−	X	−	X	−	−	−	−	−
Eastern Wood Pewee	−	−	X	−	−	−	X	X	X	−	−	−	−	−
Least Flycatcher	X	X	X	X	X	X	X	X	X	X	X	−	−	−
Eastern Phoebe	X	X	X	X	X	X	X	X	X	X	X	−	X	X
Great Crested Flycatcher	X	X	X	X	X	X	X	X	X	X	X	X	X	X
Eastern Kingbird	X	X	X	X	X	X	X	X	X	X	X	X	−	X
Horned Lark	X	X	X	−	X	X	X	X	X	X	X	X	X	X
Purple Martin	X	X	X	−	X	X	X	X	X	X	X	X	X	X
Tree Swallow	X	X	X	X	X	X	X	X	X	X	X	X	X	X
Northern Rough-winged Swallow	X	X	X	X	X	X	X	X	X	X	X	X	X	X
Bank Swallow	−	X	X	−	X	X	X	X	X	X	X	X	X	X
Cliff Swallow	−	X	−	X	X	X	−	−	X	X	X	−	X	X
Barn Swallow	X	X	X	X	X	X	X	X	X	X	X	X	X	X
Blue Jay	X	X	X	X	X	X	X	X	X	X	X	X	X	X
American Crow	X	X	X	X	X	X	X	X	X	X	X	X	X	X
Common Raven	−	−	−	−	−	−	−	−	−	−	−	−	−	−
Black-capped Chickadee	X	X	X	X	X	X	X	X	X	X	X	X	X	X
Red-breasted Nuthatch	X	−	X	−	−	−	−	−	−	X	−	−	−	X
White-breasted Nuthatch	X	X	X	X	X	X	X	X	X	X	X	X	X	X
Brown Creeper	−	X	X	X	−	−	−	−	−	−	−	−	−	X
House Wren	X	X	X	X	X	X	X	X	X	X	X	X	X	X
Winter Wren	−	X	X	−	−	−	−	−	−	−	−	−	−	−
Sedge Wren	X	X	X	−	X	−	X	−	X	X	−	X	−	−
Marsh Wren	X	X	X	−	X	−	X	−	X	X	−	X	−	−
Ruby-crowned Kinglet	X	X	X	X	X	X	X	X	−	X	−	−	−	X
Blue-gray Gnatcatcher	X	X	X	−	X	X	X	X	X	X	X	X	−	X
Eastern Bluebird	X	X	X	X	X	X	X	X	X	X	X	X	X	X
Veery	X	X	X	X	X	−	X	X	−	X	−	−	X	X
Gray-cheeked Thrush	−	−	X	X	−	X	X	X	X	X	−	−	−	−
Swainson's Thrush	−	X	X	X	X	−	X	X	X	−	−	X	−	X
Hermit Thrush	X	X	X	−	−	−	X	X	X	−	−	−	−	−
Wood Thrush	X	X	X	X	X	X	X	X	X	X	X	X	−	X
American Robin	X	X	X	X	X	X	X	X	X	X	X	X	X	X
Gray Catbird	X	X	X	X	X	X	X	X	X	X	X	X	X	X
Brown Thrasher	X	X	X	X	X	X	X	X	X	X	X	X	X	X
Cedar Waxwing	−	X	X	X	−	−	X	X	X	X	X	X	X	X
European Starling	X	X	X	X	X	X	X	X	X	X	X	X	X	X
Solitary Vireo	−	−	X	−	X	X	−	X	−	−	−	−	−	−
Yellow-throated Vireo	X	−	X	X	X	−	X	−	X	X	−	−	−	−
Warbling Vireo	X	X	X	−	X	X	X	X	X	X	X	X	X	−
Red-eyed Vireo	X	X	X	X	−	X	X	X	X	X	X	X	X	−
Blue-winged Warbler	−	−	X	−	X	X	X	−	X	X	−	X	−	−
Golden-winged Warbler	−	X	X	−	−	−	X	X	X	X	−	−	−	−
Tennessee Warbler	X	X	X	X	X	−	X	X	X	X	−	X	−	X
Nashville Warbler	X	X	X	X	X	X	X	X	X	X	X	X	−	X
Northern Parula Warbler	−	X	X	−	X	X	X	X	−	X	−	−	−	X
Yellow Warbler	X	X	X	X	X	X	X	X	X	X	X	X	X	X
Chestnut-sided Warbler	−	X	X	X	X	−	X	X	X	X	−	X	X	X
Magnolia Warbler	X	X	X	X	X	−	X	X	X	X	−	X	−	X
Cape May Warbler	X	X	X	−	X	−	X	X	X	X	−	X	X	−

(continued)

Table 3. *Continued*

Species	Calumet Co.	Winnebago Co.	Fond du Lac Co.	Shiocton	Horicon	Ozaukee Co.	Racine/Kenosha	Plymouth	Waukesha Co.	Oconomowoc	Lake Geneva	Lake Mills	Rock Co.	Kenosha Co.
Black-throated Blue Warbler	—	—	—	—	—	—	X	X	—	—	—	—	—	X
Yellow-rumped Warbler	X	X	X	X	X	X	X	X	X	X	X	—	—	X
Black-throated Green Warbler	X	X	X	X	X	X	X	X	X	X	—	X	—	X
Blackburnian Warbler	X	X	X	X	X	X	X	X	X	X	X	—	—	X
Pine Warbler	—	—	—	—	—	—	—	X	—	—	—	—	—	—
Palm Warbler	—	X	X	X	X	X	X	X	X	X	X	X	X	X
Bay-breasted Warbler	—	X	X	X	X	—	X	X	X	—	—	X	—	X
Blackpoll Warbler	—	—	X	X	X	—	X	X	X	—	—	—	—	X
Cerulean Warbler	—	—	X	—	—	—	—	X	X	X	—	—	—	X
Black-and-White Warbler	X	X	X	X	X	—	X	—	X	X	—	X	X	X
American Redstart	—	X	X	X	X	—	X	X	X	X	—	X	X	X
Ovenbird	X	X	X	X	X	X	X	X	X	X	X	X	—	X
Northern Waterthrush	—	X	X	X	X	X	X	X	—	—	X	—	X	X
Connecticut Warbler	—	—	—	—	—	—	—	X	X	—	—	X	—	X
Mourning Warbler	—	—	X	—	—	—	X	—	—	—	—	X	—	X
Common Yellowthroat	X	X	X	X	X	X	X	X	X	X	X	X	X	X
Wilson's Warbler	X	X	X	X	X	—	X	X	X	—	—	—	—	—
Canada Warbler	—	—	X	X	—	—	X	X	X	—	—	X	—	X
Scarlet Tanager	X	X	X	X	—	X	X	X	X	X	X	X	X	X
Northern Cardinal	X	X	X	X	X	X	X	X	X	X	X	X	X	X
Rose-breasted Grosbeak	X	X	X	X	X	X	X	X	X	X	X	X	X	X
Indigo Bunting	X	X	X	X	X	—	X	X	X	X	X	—	X	X
Rufous-sided Towhee	—	X	X	X	X	X	X	X	X	X	X	X	X	X
Chipping Sparrow	X	X	X	X	X	X	X	X	X	X	X	X	X	X
Clay-colored Sparrow	—	X	—	—	—	X	—	—	—	—	—	—	—	—
Field Sparrow	X	X	X	X	X	X	X	X	X	X	X	X	—	—
Vesper Sparrow	X	X	X	—	—	X	X	X	—	X	X	—	—	—
Savannah Sparrow	X	X	X	—	X	X	X	X	X	X	X	X	—	—
Grasshopper Sparrow	—	—	X	—	X	X	—	—	X	X	X	—	—	—
Henslow's Sparrow	X	X	—	—	—	—	X	—	X	X	—	—	—	—
Le Conte's Sparrow	—	X	—	—	—	—	—	—	—	—	—	—	—	—
Song Sparrow	X	X	X	X	X	X	X	X	X	X	X	X	X	X
Lincoln's Sparrow	X	X	X	—	X	X	X	—	—	X	—	—	—	X
Swamp Sparrow	X	X	X	—	X	X	X	X	X	X	X	—	—	X
White-throated Sparrow	X	X	X	X	X	X	X	X	X	X	X	X	X	X
White-crowned Sparrow	X	X	X	—	X	X	X	X	X	X	X	X	X	X
Dark-eyed Junco	—	X	—	—	—	—	X	—	—	—	—	—	—	—
Bobolink	X	X	X	—	X	X	X	X	X	X	X	X	—	X
Red-winged Blackbird	X	X	X	X	X	X	X	X	X	X	X	X	X	X
Eastern Meadowlark	X	X	X	X	X	X	X	X	X	X	X	X	X	X
Western Meadowlark	X	X	X	—	X	—	—	—	X	X	—	—	X	—
Yellow-headed Blackbird	X	X	X	—	X	—	X	X	X	X	—	X	—	X
Brewer's Blackbird	—	X	—	—	X	—	—	X	X	—	—	—	—	X
Common Grackle	X	X	X	X	X	X	X	X	X	X	X	X	X	X
Brown-headed Cowbird	X	X	X	X	X	X	X	X	X	X	X	X	X	X
Northern Oriole	X	X	X	X	X	X	X	X	X	X	X	X	X	X
Purple Finch	—	X	X	X	X	—	X	X	—	X	—	X	—	X
House Finch	X	X	X	X	X	X	X	X	X	X	X	X	X	X
Pine Siskin	—	X	—	—	—	—	X	—	—	X	—	—	—	—
American Goldfinch	X	X	X	X	X	X	X	X	X	X	X	X	X	X
Evening Grosbeak	—	—	—	—	—	—	—	—	—	—	—	—	—	—
House Sparrow	X	X	X	X	X	X	X	X	X	X	X	X	X	X

Table 4. Species seen on 4 or fewer counts, May Count 1992.

Species	Counts
Horned Grebe	Ashland/Bayfield
Red-necked Grebe	Burnett, Winnebago
American White Pelican	Ashland/Bayfield
Cattle Egret	Ashland/Bayfield

(*continued*)

Table 4. *Continued*

Species	Counts
Tundra Swan	Shawano, Winnebago, Kenosha
Trumpeter Swan	Portage
Cinnamon Teal	Lake Mills
Black Scoter	Ashland/Bayfield
Red-breasted Merganser	Ashland/Bayfield, Winnebago, Ozaukee, Racine/Kenosha
Northern Goshawk	Oxbo/Fifield, Oconto, Racine/Kenosha
Rough-legged Hawk	Burnett, Shawano, Horicon
Merlin	Ashland/Bayfield, Oconomowoc
Gray Partridge	Portage, Winnebago
Greater Prairie-Chicken	Marathon, Portage, Taylor
Sharp-tailed Grouse	Burnett, Taylor, Oxbo/Fifield
Northern Bobwhite	Winnebago, Racine/Kenosha
King Rail	Fond du Lac
Common Moorhen	Oconto, Winnebago, Horicon, Lake Geneva
Black-bellied Plover	Ashland/Bayfield, Vilas, Horicon, Racine/Kenosha
Lesser Golden Plover	Horicon
Piping Plover	Racine/Kenosha
Hudsonian Godwit	Burnett, Shawano
Ruddy Turnstone	Winnebago, Racine/Kenosha, Kenosha
Sanderling	Ashland/Bayfield, Racine/Kenosha, Kenosha
White-rumped Sandpiper	Burnett, Racine/Kenosha
Baird's Sandpiper	Ashland/Bayfield, Calumet
Wilson's Phalarope	Calumet, Winnebago, Fond du Lac, Horicon
Red-necked Phalarope	Winnebago
Franklin's Gull	Plymouth
Glaucous Gull	Winnebago
Eastern Screech-Owl	Winnebago, Racine/Kenosha, Oconomowoc
Long-eared Owl	Oconto
Short-eared Owl	Kenosha
Northern Saw-whet Owl	Oxbo/Fifield, Vilas
Black-backed Woodpecker	Oxbo/Fifield
Olive-sided Flycatcher	Racine/Kenosha, Oconto, Plymouth, Waukesha
Yellow-bellied Flycatcher	Vilas, Plymouth, Waukesha
Acadian Flycatcher	Waukesha, Fond du Lac
Alder Flycatcher	Marathon, Vilas
Willow Flycatcher	Winnebago, Racine/Kenosha
Gray Jay	Oxbo/Fifield, Vilas
Boreal Chickadee	Vilas
Tufted Titmouse	Marathon, Oconomowoc
Carolina Wren	Racine/Kenosha
Golden-crowned Kinglet	Oxbo/Fifield, Vilas, Shawano
Mockingbird	Burnett, Shawano
Water Pipit	Shawano, Winnebago, Oconto
Loggerhead Shrike	Oconto
White-eyed Vireo	Waukesha, Racine/Kenosha
Philadelphia Vireo	Winnebago, Fond du Lac, Plymouth, Shiocton
Orange-crowned Warbler	Winnebago, Fond du Lac, Plymouth
Prothonotary Warbler	Oconomowoc
Louisiana Waterthrush	Buffalo, Racine/Kenosha
Kentucky Warbler	Fond du Lac, Plymouth, Waukesha
Hooded Warbler	Ashland/Bayfield, Horicon, Racine/Kenosha, Waukesha
Western Tanager	Fond du Lac
American Tree Sparrow	Lake Geneva

(continued)

Table 4. *Continued*

Species	Counts
Lark Sparrow	Oconomowoc
Fox Sparrow	Racine/Kenosha, Oconomowoc, Kenosha
Harris' Sparrow	Oxbo/Fifield, Taylor
Lapland Longspur	Winnebago, Fond du Lac, Horicon
Orchard Oriole	Racine/Kenosha, Plymouth, Ozaukee
Common Redpoll	Oxbo/Fifield

Jim Frank
  4339 West Laverna Ave.
  Mequon, WI 53092

Barrow's Goldeneye *by Frank Mittelstadt.*

"By the Wayside"

Reports of Common Loon, Red-necked Grebe, Eared Grebe, Snowy Egret, Little Blue Heron, Ross' Goose, Cinnamon Teal, Eurasian Wigeon, Harlequin Duck, Swallow-tailed Kite, Black-shouldered Kite, Swainson's Hawk, King Rail, Yellow Rail, Piping Plover, Short-billed Dowitcher, Purple Sandpiper, Laughing Gull, Thayer's Gull, Iceland Gull, Lesser Black-backed Gull, Great Black-backed Gull, Northern Hawk-owl, Chuck-will's-widow, Vermillion Flycatcher, Tree Swallow, Black-billed Magpie, Carolina Wren, Northern Mockingbird, Yellow-throated Warbler, Worm-eating Warbler, Sharp-tailed Sparrow and Rusty Blackbird.

COMMON LOON CHICKS LEAVE NATAL LAKE BEFORE FLEDGING

August 1991, Vilas County George Lake—Common Loons show biparental care of their chicks, both parents sharing in feeding and protection until the chicks fledge around 12 weeks post-hatching. Past observations suggest that loon chicks are reared on their natal lakes. On large lakes occupied by more than one territorial pair, rearing typically occurs in nursery areas located within a pair's territory but some distance from the nesting site (J.W. McIntyre, *J. Field Ornith.* 54:247–253, 1983). On smaller, single-pair lakes, adults use their entire nesting lake as a chick nursery. We report here an observation of two recently-banded loon chicks abandoning their small natal lake for an adjacent larger lake.

The chicks were color-banded at about five weeks of age on George Lake (46°09′N, 89°18′W), a 4.8 ha, moderately shallow lake 7 km west of Land-O-Lakes, Vilas County, Wisconsin. This lake has been used as a nesting lake by the same pair of loons since at least 1988 (the male identified by vocal-tagging; Miller, unpublished data). The pair has hatched one or two chicks on George Lake in three of the four seasons we have studied them. However, our observation of the pair in past years did not extend beyond early August, so we cannot confirm that chicks fledged from the lake.

George Lake lies adjacent to the much larger and deeper Black Oak Lake (222.3 ha). Significantly, during each of the four seasons the pair nesting on George Lake has been studied, it has actively defended and fed on approximately half of Black Oak Lake in addition to defending and nesting on George Lake (Miller, unpublished data). This pair is one of several loon pairs recently discovered to show such multiple-lake territoriality (C.E. Miller and T. Dring, *1987 Conf. Common Loon Res. and Mgmt.*, 1988, J.L. Belant, *Passenger Pigeon* 53:187–188, 1991).

George and Black Oak Lakes are 92 m apart, separated by dense wetland vegetation, a county highway (Vilas County Highway B), a paved parking lot and a sand beach. Despite these obstacles, the two chicks from George Lake relocated to Black Oak Lake where, accompanied by their parents, they were observed by Wentz and McCarthy on 11 August 1991. The chicks, still in their second down plumage, were incapable of flight. Although loons are poorly designed for terrestrial locomotion, we conclude that the chicks moved overland from George Lake to Black Oak Lake.

J.W. McIntyre (*The Common Loon: Spirit of Northern Lakes*, U. Minn. Press, 1988) recounts two instances of chicks leaving a small lake for a larger one, including one occasion when loon chicks moving overland were picked up by a human observer and carried to a nearby lake. The observation we report is the first known observation of color-marked Common Loon chicks relocating from their natal lake without apparent human intervention. Confirmation of chick identity in the present case allows us to speculate on an explanation for the chicks' interlake movement.

J.F. Barr (unpubl. Ph.D. thesis, Univ. of Guelph, Ontario, 1973) estimates that for typical northern oligotrophic lakes a surface area of 40–55 ha is necessary to provide sufficient food (estimated in kg) for a loon pair and two chicks. Two chicks alone (adults feeding themselves elsewhere) would need a lake of approximately 30 ha. Even if George Lake were substantially above average in fish productivity, at 4.8 ha available food may well have been below minimum sufficiency even for the two chicks.

Interlake chick movement and the phenomenon of multiple-lake territory defense thus may be related. Multiple-lake defense may function, in part, to provide a separate feeding area for adult loons choosing to nest on very small lakes or to reserve an alternate nursery location for chicks should the need arise. That loon chicks are capable of moving overland for at least the distance required here indicates the practical feasibility of such an explanation.

Harry and Judy Keller provided timely logistical support making this observation possible. The George Lake loon chicks were banded by David Evers. Miller and Wentz individually have received research funding for several on-going projects from the North American Loon Fund, Sigurd Olson Environmental Institute, the Michigan Department of Natural Resources (Miller), the Frank M. Chapman Memorial Fund (Wentz), and the Michigan Loon Preservation Association.— *C. Edward Miller and Mary M. McCarthy, Biology Department, Governors State University, University Park, IL 60466; Lauren E. Wentz, Department of Biology, University of Wisconsin-Whitewater, Whitewater, WI 53190.*

RED-NECKED GREBE

18 March 1992, Dane County, Lake Mendota—In the northwest corner of the bay I noted a grebe that was swimming but not diving. I observed a thick long bill almost the length of the bird's head. I noted the white cheek and throat patch contrasting with the dusky grayish neck. The back of the neck and the back were dark while the sides of the bird were grayish white. The eye was dark. The bird swam above water the entire viewing time. I lost sight of the bird when my view was obstructed by a large willow tree. I never saw the bird fly.—*Kay Burcar, 5136 Enchanted Valley Rd, Cross Plains, WI 53528.*

EARED GREBE

18 April 1992, Manitowoc County, Manitowoc Marina—I first noted the small grebe walking back to my truck about 50–75 yards off the north breakwater. I made a mental note about the lack of extensive white in the throat and cheek area which is a field mark of the more common Horned Grebes which I had observed earlier in the day. This bird was in winter plumage. The white that was present was limited to the chin area and lower breast area at the water line. The white in the chin and lower breast was broken by an extensive area of light brown color in the upper throat to upper breast. There was also no white on the cheek area at all. In fact when the bird tucked its head to rest there was no white showing in the head area whatsoever. I believe if this would have been a Horned Grebe the white in its cheek up to its eye line would have showed. The bird never dove nor ventured more than

50–75 yards away, spent its time preening and resting.—*Scott J. Baughman, 2016A N. 8th Street, Sheboygan, WI 53081.*

SNOWY EGRET

24 April 1992, Dodge County, Horicon Marsh—On 4-24-92 about 1:30 P.M. I observed a Snowy Egret from a distance of fifty yards near the pond on Old Marsh Road in Horicon Marsh of Dodge Co. I first saw the bird standing in shallow water and noted its small size. The bird flushed immediately so I could easily observe the yellow feet. The small size of this bird compared to several nearby Great Egrets and the bright yellow feet confirmed the identification.—*Kay Burcar, 5136 Enchanted Valley Rd, Cross Plains, WI 53528.*

LITTLE BLUE HERON

18 April 1992, Manitowoc County, 0.4 mi south of CTH F on CTH LS—While driving north on CTH LS I saw a dark colored wading bird in a partially flooded field. The bird was much darker than the more common Great Blue Heron and appeared to be somewhat smaller. I set my window mount scope (20× Bushnel) up and noted the slate blue appearance and lack of white anywhere on the bird. Its bill was two tone in color with the base being about the same color as the mantle. This coloring extended about 3/4 the length with the tip being darker almost black. The legs appeared to be greenish gray in color. The neck and head on the bird was a darker color than the rest of the bird's slate blue color. It was quite active feeding in the small pond, it was alone. It appeared to be in nonbreeding plumage. I also set up my

Bausch and Lomb 8080 mirror scope with 30mm eyepiece (26×). The pond and bird were between 150–200 yards from the edge of the road. I left the bird as I found it (feeding) returned 2 hours later to find him still present and still active feeding.—*Scott J. Baughman, 2016A N. 8th Street, Sheboygan, WI 53081.*

ROSS' GOOSE

15 March 1992, Columbia County, Schoeneberg Marsh—From Harvey Road, north of STH 60, there was an area of open water, approximately 150 yards from the road, densely occupied with Canada Geese and other waterfowl. While searching through these birds with a zoom spotting scope set to 22×, I observed Greater White-fronted Geese, both phases of Snow Geese, several species of ducks, and a small white goose with black primaries. At this time of day the lighting of the birds was ideal, and size comparison with the aforementioned species was facilitated by their density. In size, the small goose was three-fourths the size of the Snow Geese and comparable to nearby Mallards. It swam continuously during my observation but stayed in the vicinity of Snow Geese. At certain angles the black "grin" of the Snow Geese was evident, but this characteristic was not present on the smaller goose. Its bill was much shorter, dull pink in coloration and appeared discolored near the base. The bird had a rounder head than the Snow Geese. Based on size comparison and bill characteristics, I conclude this was a Ross' Goose.—*Thomas C. Wood, 8895E N. 91st St, Milwaukee, WI 53224.*

17 March 1992, Columbia County, Schoeneberg Marsh—When I arrived at

the bend in Harvey Road at Schoeneberg marsh I immediately spotted three white geese among several thousand Canada Geese. Two of these geese were about ten feet distance from each other. I noted that one had a clean white head and neck plumage while the other had considerable grayish patches on these areas. I concentrated on the all white bird noting that this bird was about two-thirds the size of the other white goose. The bill of this bird was shorter and stubbier than that of the other two geese. It also had no dark line on the lower mandible. When the bird stood on the ice, I noted that the legs were brighter pink than that of the proximate Snow Goose. The eye was dark. The size comparison was so striking as the birds walked along the ice, then swam in some open water in full view for several minutes. I continued to watch the three geese for about 30 minutes until a flock of Canada Geese took off with the small white goose trailing along. When the bird flew, I noted the much faster wing beat of the white goose when compared to Canada Geese as there were no other Snow Geese that flew at this time to compare. When the geese flew, I also heard distinctly the different call of the white goose as it called when it flew quite close to our vantage point. The geese headed north and did to return to the area while we were there.—*Kay Burcar, 5136 Enchanted Valley Rd, Cross Plains, WI 53528.*

25 March 1992, Dane County, Barney Lake—When I first arrived at the pond I saw a small white goose among about 300 Canada Geese. For the first fifteen minutes, the bird rested with its head tucked the entire time so I was unable to identify the bird. I left the area to call a friend about the bird and returned in fifteen minutes. Although the bird was still resting when I returned, a group of Canada Geese flew into the area and disturbed the resting geese. When the white goose lifted its head I noted the small rounded head, short neck, and very small stubby bill. I also observed that the bill had no black line on the lower mandible. When the bird preened, I noted the clean all white plumage with black primaries, dark eye, and dark pinkish legs and bill. The white goose, which was less than half the size of some of the Canadas, left the shoreline and began to swim. I was able to see the bird without any obstructions as it swam from the eastern shore to the southwestern shore. At this point the bird left the water to feed in the short pasture grass. I continued to watch the goose as it swam back to the eastern shore and left the water to rest again in the grass. When the bird walked on shore, the size comparison was again noted with the Canadas. Some small Canadas were approximately the same size as the white goose while others were more than twice its size. I also noted that the goose was only slightly longer than some Northern Shovelers in the area. When the bird moved along the shore, it walked quickly almost acting like a duck rather than a goose. I continued to watch the goose for about an hour. On 3-26-92 I returned to Lake Barney for another possible sighting about 7:00 A.M. I immediately spotted the white goose and again noted the above features. I stayed in the area until 8:45 A.M. and the goose never left. On 3-27-92 I returned again to Lake Barney about 7:00 A.M. At first I was unable to spot the bird among about

100 Canada Geese that were tightly grouped resting on ice on the eastern shore. In about fifteen minutes when other geese flew in, the resting group was disturbed and the white goose appeared among them. I watched the bird for about thirty minutes leaving the area about 7:45 A.M.—*Kay Burcar, 5136 Enchanted Valley Rd, Cross Plains, 53528.*

26 March 1992, Dane County, Barney Lake—When we arrived at Lake Barney, we saw a flock of 100+ Canada Geese feeding on a grassy knoll just east of the lake. With the Canadas was a white goose, noticeably smaller than the Canadas. We set up our telescopes and watched the birds for 30 minutes from a distance estimated at 250–300 yards. When the bird was actively feeding (which was most of the observation time), we could not make out clearly the color and shape of the bill, the shape of the head and neck, nor the color of the legs. We saw only the all-white body, plus two black areas at the posterior end of the bird which we took to be black wing tips. While feeding, the bird walked rapidly from one spot to another.

It was on the rare occasions when the bird stood erect that we added the following field marks: (1) the bill was short, stubby, and reddish; (2) the top of the head was rounded; (3) the neck was unusually short for a goose; and (4) the legs were reddish. We checked carefully for any trace of a dark "grinning patch" along the sides of the bill, but saw no trace.

The entire flock flew from the knoll to the lake during the latter part of the observation period; but we were so engrossed in writing up our notes that we failed to see the bird in flight. In its swimming pose the bird displayed a slightly longer neck than what we had previously seen; but we agreed that the goose had an unusually short neck.— *James Hale, 5401 Raymond Road, Madison, WI 53711; Sam Robbins, 14 S. Roby Road, Madison, WI 53705.*

CINNAMON TEAL

22 April 1992, Columbia County, Schoeneberg Marsh—On 4-22-92 between 6:00 and 6:30 A.M. at Schoeneberg marsh I observed a male Cinnamon Teal among about 100 Blue-winged Teals from a distance of less than 50 yards. I saw the dark maroon head, neck, breast, and sides of the bird. The reddish color of the head appeared somewhat darker than that of the neck and breast. I noted the large black shoveler-like bill that was noticeably larger than that of the bluewing teal. When the bird flushed, I noted the large blue patch on the front part of the wing. The undertail coverts were black, and the back was dark with two lighter stripes along the lower back. The eye was dark. I observed the bird for about 30 minutes as it swam in a small pond, then watched it fly. On 4–25 and 4–27 I again saw this bird in the same location.—*Kay Burcar, 5136 Enchanted Valley Rd, Cross Plains, WI 53528.*

6 May 1992, Dodge County, Rock River—Cinnamon red head and underparts Back is brown mottling. Bright red eye. Bill blackish colored and spatulate shaped. In flight has light blue color on forward edge of wing and a green speculum. Although numerous Blue-winged Teal are in the area the Cinnamon is at some distance from the Blue-winged. It is with a fe-

male teal—and the two associate throughout the two hours. I would to be certain that the female was also a Cinnamon Teal.—*Robert C. Domagalski, W140 N8508 Lilly Rd, Menomonee Falls, WI 53051.*

7 May 1992, Dodge County, Ashippun—Having no luck on the first swing through the flooded areas off the Rock River, I resumed birding at the beginning of my route I started an hour before. This time 2 Cinnamon Teal were with the Blue-winged Teal.

The drake was quite obvious—the size of the Blue-winged Teal, but bright orange brown through the head, neck and sides. The back and wings (folded) were mottled brown. The eye was vivid red. The gray bill was a bit longer than a Blue-winged Teal's.

The shape of the hen was the same as the drake—like a Blue-winged Teal but with a longer gray bill than the hen Blue-winged Teal. In addition, the overall mottled brown color instead of having a gray overcast like the Blue-winged Teal had a yellowish wash.—*Jim Frank, 4339 W. Laverna Ave., Mequon, WI 53092.*

14 May 1992, Jefferson County, east of Aztalan—When I spotted this bird while scanning the shallow pond for shorebirds, my first reaction upon seeing the dark red head and forehead nearly sloping to a dark bill was, what is a Canvasback doing on a pond like this? The rest of the bird was nearly hidden in emergent vegetation, but it was instantly obvious the bird was about the size of the nearby Blue-winged Teal and that its back, neck and lower parts were all the same color as its head, perhaps just a shade lighter, and that the color was more of a deep cinnamon rather than red. The bird dabbled continuously as it moved in and out of thicker and sparser vegetation. The eye appeared to be dark and the wings seemed to have a mix of white and black (or other dark color), but in 30 minutes of observation the bird never flew or preened. At one point, it slept; with a nearby Blue-winged Teal for comparison, it had the same general aspect and was perhaps slightly larger. When I asked Audrey Schlender, whom I was doing a May Day count with, to take a look at the bird I had in the scope she identified it immediately as a male Cinnamon Teal.—*Karen Etter Hale, 517 Tower Street, Lake Mills, WI 53551.*

CINNAMON TEAL × BLUE-WINGED TEAL HYBRID

14 April 1992, Dane County, Nine Springs—When I saw about six Blue-winged Teal swimming in the canal north of the road I observed one bird that had cinnamon brown sides rather than the dull gray brown of the others. This color feature was quite striking, however, I also noted that the bird had the white crescent on its face. The head was greenish-black rather than cinnamon. Along the upper back there was a white line unlike the Blue-winged Teals. Also there was only a very little white patch just in front of the under tail coverts. The bill was black and about one-fourth larger than that of the Blue-winged Teals.—*Kay Burcar, 5136 Enchanted Valley Rd, Cross Plains, WI 53528.*

EURASIAN WIGEON

3 March 1992, Dane County, Crystal Lake—My brother, Scott, and I ar-

rived, at the southeast corner of Crystal Lake, at about 12:25 pm. We had just been to Madison where Scott purchased a new spotting scope. We were viewing the lake from off Crystal Lake Road, where several species of ducks could be seen, from dabblers to divers. Most of the ducks were in the middle of the lake or in a bay on the northeast side of the lake, quite a ways off (.3-.4 miles). The day was cool so viewing with a spotting scope at high power, heat waves were not a problem. We could see many American Wigeon, so we kept the scope on this group of ducks expecting the *male* Eurasian to be with these ducks in particular. It didn't take long (about 10 min.) to find a good candidate, and even at the distance we were confident of our identification.

(All field marks here are described based on adult male birds) First the bird had a much different head color than the rest of the wigeons. This is the feature, on Eurasian Wigeon, that is best seen and because of our distance from the birds, other marking such as the flanks and crown color were not as easily seen. The head on the Eurasian showed a rich chestnut color, quite different then the gray of the other wigeons. No other wigeon showed any of this rusty/chestnut color. Once the Eurasian Wigeon was spotted we went to high power on our scopes; 45× and 42×. At this power we again noted the head color but could not safely say the crown stripe was in fact cream colored so we began studying the flanks of the two species (this being one of the other identification keys). The Eurasian showed a lighter flank color than the other wigeons. It appeared to be gray-grayish, lighter colored anyway, where the

American Wigeons had a browner flanks, quite different. The two species are opposite in these two features: gray flanks & chestnut head on the Eurasian and gray head & chestnut flanks on the American. Based on these observations we are confident that we were observing an adult male Eurasian Wigeon.

Other field marks noted in both species include: gray-brown back color, black undertail coverts bordered anteriorly with a white vertical mark. Bill markings were not noted and because the birds never took flight, colors and patterns were never noted.—*Jeffrey L. Baughman, W8985 CTH SS, Adell, WI 53001.*

13 March 1992, Dane County, Crystal Lake—After checking over 60 wigeons throughout the entire area of Fish & Crystal lakes, and Marx pond, I was scoping the last area long the northern shoreline of Crystal Lake among fallen logs. About 3:30 P.M. I spotted a reddish-headed duck among several dozen Mallards, a few Northern Shovelers, and about ten American Wigeons. Since I was scoping from the southern shoreline, the distance was perhaps 500 yards or more, however, the conditions were near perfect for viewing across the entire lake. Since I was looking for this particular bird, I was able to identify it readily even from this distance. I observed the reddish-brown head with a light colored forehead extending into the crown. I noted the buffy-brown breast, and grayish sides and back. The black tail contrasted with the lighter sides and there was a white patch between the tail and the sides. After about fifteen minutes since I wanted to see this bird at a closer distance, I traveled to a private road on the north side of Crystal Lake. Af-

ter asking permission from the landowner to scope the area from their roadway, I again spotted the bird from a distance of 100 yards of less. From this vantage point I again observed the reddish head and creamish colored forehead and crown. I noted the back of the head was entirely reddish-brown as the creamy patch ended on the crown. I observed the white scapulars which separated the gray back and sides. The white patch between the sides and black tail formed somewhat of a band. I noted the quite blueish color of the bill with a small black nail on the distal end. The eye was dark. After another fifteen minutes, all the birds in the area were flushed by the appearance of the landowner's dog. When the birds flew, they headed in the direction of the southern end of the lake, however, I was unable to relocate the bird. On 3-16-92 I again saw this bird swimming with many other American Wigeons at 9:30 A.M. in the same location.—*Kay Burcar, 5136 Enchanted Valley Rd, Cross Plains, WI 53528.*

HARLEQUIN DUCK

17 May 1992, Sheboygan County, Sheboygan River—Bird was found standing on rocks on the south side of the south pier in the Sheboygan Marina. The distinctive head pattern was quite visible. Large white patch at base of bill that runs up the bird's forehead and above the eye was very apparent at the close range we observed the bird. All the other distinctive head patterning and colors were also observed; the single white dot near the ear and vertical white line along the side of the bird's head was also present. The rusty color found near the top of the head that bleeds from the aforementioned white forehead line, was also noted. The flanks were also colored with this same rusty hue. The distinctive patterning of feathers on the breast of the bird were also noted. The two striking white lines that run across the breast, one like a necklace on the upper breast, the other runs vertically along the sides of the breast.—*Scott J. Baughman, 2016A N. 8th St, Sheboygan, WI 53081.*

SWALLOW-TAILED KITE

12 May 1992, Marquette County, Harrisville—On Tuesday, May 12, 1992 at about 4:30 P.M. in the afternoon I was driving my van west on CTY J between Harrisville and Westfield. It was an overcast, breezy (5–7 knots) 70° day. There had just been scattered thundershowers. The land is fairly unbroken pastures with oak/pine woods and marsh tamarack. My attention was drawn to a large, conspicuous bird I have never seen in this area. It was flying in a somewhat erratically, but coarsing flight as if it were catching insects—well above the height of the trees. This bird was observed in the company of other smaller birds that appeared to be doing the same thing.

I saw a bird with a deep forked tail that was dark in color. The dark wing tips and deeply forked tail contrasted greatly with the rest of the body.

The bird I saw was black and white. The black extended from the trailing edge of the wing to the wing-tips and a black tail. The bird was the size of a big redtail—a hearty bird.

The bird I saw was a Swallow-tailed Kite. I have seen them in Florida.—*Rebecca Ratering, 515 Gold St., Green Lake, WI 54941.*

BLACK-SHOULDERED KITE

10 April 1992, Monroe County, Tomah—I did not get a good look at the underwing, but the bird started to hover about a foot from the ground and what I did see is a good view of the entire dorsal surface of the bird. The general overall color was light-gray (even lighter than the male harrier, at least that was my impression). My first thought was "Northern Harrier," but then the tail did not seem as long proportionately. The next field mark outstandingly was the black patches starting at the end in each wing and continuing inward along the leading edge. The back of the bird was light-gray; I didn't notice much contrast between the head, tail and back, but by this time the bird was in the 4 o'clock position and I had to get my eyes back on the road.—*Daniel E. Krysiak, 4687 N. 69th St., Milwaukee, WI 53218.*

SWAINSON'S HAWK

26 May 1992, Dane County, Fitchburg—About 200 yards west of my vantage point, a buteo was alternately soaring and flapping. It may have been reacting somewhat to a pursing grackle. Particularly noticeable were the long straight wings somewhat tapered near tips—quite unlike the rounded tips I am used to seeing on red-tails and broad-wings. The hawk appeared to be the size of a red-tail.

Conspicuous on the under surface of the wings also was a distinct two-toned pattern of light wing linings and dark flight feathers. The wing linings were off-white rather than gleaming white, providing a sharp contrast to the dark grayish-brown of the flight feathers.

Another conspicuous feature was the dark coloration of the upper breast. I could never be certain if the dark area extended upward to include the throat, but it ended abruptly half way down the breast. The color appeared browner than the gray-brown of the flight feathers. The belly was whitish.

The tail was short and fanned, typical for buteos. Seen from below, there was a dark terminal band, plus three or four very narrow bands. Twice when the bird wheeled, I saw the same terminal band on the upper surface of the tail, and a light area at the base of the tail. This light area was seen only in glimpses, but was less noticeable than the white rumps I have seen on harriers and rough-legs.

The behavior of the hawk was unusual. First it did some flapping when pursued briefly by the grackle. When the grackle left, the hawk did some circular gliding on slightly tilted wings. Then it faced north and did some moderately vigorous flapping. It was as if it was making no progress against a stiff wind; but I was not aware of anything stronger than a slight breeze. The flapping was more like slow-motion hovering. After another brief period of circular gliding, there was another period of hovering lasting 15–30 seconds, after which the hawk sailed out of sight.—*Sam Robbins, 14 S. Roby Road, Madison, WI 53705.*

KING RAIL

3, 14, 16 May 1992, Dodge County, Horicon Marsh—On 5-3-92 about 8:00 P.M. on Old Marsh Road in Horicon Marsh of Dodge Co. I heard eight single steady-rhythm call notes of the King Rail. The bird had responded to the playing of a taped King Rail. Unlike the stacatto rhythm pattern of the Virginia Rail, this bird called only single notes. The sky was overcast with wind velocity between 10 and 15 mph, and the temperature was in the mid 40's. On 5-14-92 about 8:15 P.M. while I was walking near Old Marsh Road in Horicon Marsh of Dodge Co. I heard five single steady rhythm call notes of the King Rail. The sky was clear, winds were calm and the temperature was in the low 60's. The bird called on its own without the playing of a taped call. After hearing the call I went to the car for my tape player and returned to the area within 10 minutes. When I played the King Rail tape, the bird did not respond again. On 5-16-92 about 8:30 P.M. near Old Marsh Road in Horicon Marsh of Dodge Co. I heard at least two series of four to five single steady-rhythm call notes of the King Rail. I was walking on the floating cordwalk in the marsh. The sky was clear and the temperature was about 65 F. Winds were between five and ten mph from south/southwest. The calls lasted about 15 seconds after the bird had responded to the playing of a taped King Rail.—*Kay Burcar, 5136 Enchanted Valley Rd, Cross Plains, WI 53528.*

YELLOW RAIL

15 May 1992, Dodge County, Horicon Marsh—On 5-15-92 about 9:00 P.M. on Main Dike Road in Horicon Marsh of Dodge Co. I heard the calls of at least five Yellow Rails. Their calling sounded like striking two small stones together in a staccato rhythm. The call also reminded me of a single finger typist. We remained in the area for about 30 minutes all the time listening to the call of the Yellow Rails.—*Kay Burcar, 5136 Enchanted Valley Rd, Cross Plains, WI 53528.*

PIPING PLOVER

7 May 1992, Ashland County, Chequamegon Bay—We had observed several Semipalmated Plovers and students were scanning the bay with the questar. Through binoculars I saw a bird on a sandbar that I immediately suspected was a Piping Plover because of its size, actions and its very light color. Through the questar I could see the bird was a male in breeding plumage. The color of the dorsal portions was a light gray-brown and underparts were white except for a narrow black breast band (complete). A black band ran from eye to eye separating the white forehead from the gray-brown crown. The bill was orange-yellow with a black tip and legs and feet were a distinct yellow. Size was similar to the nearby Semipalmated Plovers. The bird was actively feeding and we were able to watch it for about 10 minutes. A killdeer flew in and chased the Piping Plover—to within 20 yards of where we were standing, and next to two Semipalmated Plovers. All the characteristics mentioned above could be seen through binoculars. The bird was still present when we left.—*Dick Verch, Biology Dept., Northland College, Ashland, WI 54806.*

SHORT-BILLED DOWITCHER

23 April 1992, Dodge County, "A&W" Ponds—I am writing this bird because the date, April 23, 1992, is earlier than the earliest record in Robbins (1991), which lists April 26.

One dowitcher on mudflats at edge of water, perhaps 60 yards from my car. Entire throat, breast, and belly are a solid orangish-red color with just the slightest hint of some spotting on edge of breast and throat area. Underbody (behind the legs) a pale tint of orange going to a whitish color. No sign of barring on the flanks and coverts. Back of bird has a brighter tone than the long-billeds I've been seeing and there is a noticeable orangish tinge to the back.

Did not hear any call notes—and was not about to venture into the deep mud to scare bird into calling.

Bird seems to be the hendersoni subspecies of Short-billed Dowitcher.—*Robert C. Domagalski, W140 N8508 Lilly Rd., Menomonee Falls, WI 53051.*

PURPLE SANDPIPER

4 November 1991, Sheboygan Co., Northpoint Park—On 11-4-91 at Northpoint Park in Sheboygan about 8:00 A.M. I was checking the rocky shoreline for the earlier reported Purple Sandpiper. Among about fifty Dunlins, several pectorals, several Sanderlings, a Ruddy Turnstone, and a White-rumped Sandpiper one bird about the size of a pectoral appeared from behind a rock. This bird had a stockier build than the Dunlins and pectoral. It had a smudgy gray breast with speckling directly below the upper breast. This speckling or streaking continued along the sides of the breast to the thighs and up into the undertail coverts with only a small area of white showing under the tail. Its black slightly down curved bill was about the size of the pectoral's with the basal quarter inch yellowish and its bright yellow legs were visible. A slight lighter gray eye ring was visible with an eye line that extended a quarter inch toward the back of the neck. The smokey-gray crown and head blended into a slightly scaled dark back. A whitish wing bar was noticed as well as very dark primaries. The bird flushed several times and a dark rump was noticed with the white of the undertail coverts visible. The bird fed among the rocks with the Dunlins with a probing motion sometimes immersing its entire head under the water. I watched the bird from a distance of fifty feet for approximately 45 minutes as it moved about thirty feet along the shore in open view most of the time. The weather was partly cloudy with some sunshine and occasional snowshowers. I observed this bird with Audubon Swift 8.5 by 44 binoculars. On 1-4-92 about 2:30 P.M. I again observed this individual along the Northpoint Park beach feeding in the seaweed on shore. I approached within fifty feet of the bird and noted the slight lighter ring around the eye. This field mark was not clearly visible until I observed the bird at such close range. It continued to feed in the weeds the entire viewing time of fifteen minutes. On 3-15-92 I again saw this bird and noted the above description.—*Kay Burcar, 5136 Enchanted Valley Rd, Cross Plains, WI 53528.*

LAUGHING GULL

13 May 1992, Manitowoc County, Two Rivers—While Bernie Brouchoud and I were doing our annual Big Day Bird Count at Woodland Dunes Nature Preserve, we paddled a canoe into the marsh across from the marina on the West Twin River where we always check out the gulls on the mud bars. Bernie was paddling slowly while I searched for anything unusual. This day there were hundreds of Bonaparte's Gulls sitting on the bar. As they took flight, I surveyed the flock for any which did not have the usual Bonaparte's wing pattern. I noticed one gull which was larger than the Bonaparte's, had a black head, entirely white rump and tail, and was solid gray across the back and wings; the gray shading gradually to a much darker tone at the wing tips. There was no white anywhere in the primaries nor were there any defined black areas. I only saw the bird as it wheeled past me with its dorsal surface toward me, so I did not see the underparts, bill or feet. It quickly disappeared into an enormous flock of gulls which had arisen from all over the river. I did not see it again. I have seen Laughing Gulls many times on the Gulf Coast and this gull looked just like them. I also heard some vocalizations that matched those I have heard on the Gulf from Laughing Gulls.—*Carroll Rudy, W3866 Highway H, Chilton, WI 53014.*

29 May 1992, Burnett County, Fish Lake—I noticed a medium-sized gull with a fairly dark mantle flying over the marsh. When I viewed this bird through binoculars, I was astonished to see an adult Laughing Gull, which I pointed out to Brian Boldt. This gull was almost as large as a Ring-billed Gull but it was more slender and had narrower wings. The mantle and upper surface of the wings were slate gray. Outer primaries were black and this black feathering extended further down the wing and fused directly into the gray without a white barrier. The trailing edges of the wings were white and the underside of the wings showed dusky gray near the outer primaries. As a breeding plumage adult, this gull had a black hood and white eye crescents. The fairly heavy bill was red and slightly drooped. The gull circled the marsh a few times and then flew to the east and disappeared from sight. This was a surprising inland record for this normally coastal species. Checking *Wisconsin Birdlife*, I noticed that all the previous records came from the counties along Lake Michigan.—*Mark Korducki, 4410 So. 21st Street, Milwaukee, WI 53221.*

29 May 1992, Burnett County, Grettum Flowage—My first look at the bird was in flight. Black head was noted. The bird soon banked, providing an excellent look at the back and upper wing surface. The mantle was dark gray, darker than typical Franklin's Gull (though not by much). Wingtips were black with no white spots, and the black area was larger than in typical Franklin's. In flight, the wings also showed dark coloring on undersides near the tips. Bill was dark red. Eye crescents present, but not prominent. Size was larger than typical Franklin's Gull, close to the size of a nearby Ringbilled Gull. After a brief viewing, the bird flew over some trees towards the east end of the flowage. Being reasonably certain of the i.d. we did not pursue the bird immediately, but paused to view some loons. The gull could not be relocated a few minutes later.— *Brian Boldt.*

THAYER'S GULL

15 March 1992, Milwaukee County, Milwaukee River—I first saw the bird

sitting on the ice and observed the more rounded, and delicate head when compared to the Herring Gull. The bird was just slightly smaller than the Herring Gull and had a dark eye. I also observed that the white spots on the black upper primaries were slightly larger than those of the Herring Gull. As the bird flew overhead several times, I noted the gray underprimaries. Another gull was also present which seemed to have qualities of both the Iceland and Thayer's Gull combined. Comparison: The dark eye, rounder head, and larger white spots on the primaries eliminate the Herring Gull. The black upper primaries eliminate the Iceland Gull.—*Kay Burcar, 5136 Enchanted Valley Rd, Cross Plains, WI 53528.*

15 March 1992, Manitowoc County, Two Rivers—While scoping over 500 gulls that were sitting on the ice about 75 yards distant. I noted the all black bill which appeared smaller than adjacent Herring Gulls. The bird was slightly smaller than Herring Gulls next to it. The primaries and tail were darker than the beige colored plumage of the bird. When the bird flew there was a slight indication of a band on the tail. The eye was dark. The bird resembled quite well the first year Thayer's Gull represented in the guides. The buff-beige darker colored plumage, the darker tail and primaries, and the band on the tail eliminate the Iceland Gull. The size of the bird and all dark bill eliminates the Glaucous Gull.—*Kay Burcar, 5136 Enchanted Valley Rd, Cross Plains, WI 53528.*

15, 17 March 1992, Milwaukee County, South Shore Yacht Club—The adult bird was seen in flight and on the water. It was not the same bird as the Thayer's/Iceland(?) seen on the WSO lakefront trip the Sunday previous, as this bird's mantle was quite dark. Dark eye, light underwings, rounded head, and restricted black in primaries were also noted.

The immature bird was seen standing on the sand at South Shore. The lightness of the folded primaries was immediately obvious. Buff edges of primaries could also be seen. The bill was all black. Plumage was light brown all over, the notable exception being a darker patch around the eye.—*Brian Boldt.*

25 March 1992, Douglas County, Wisconsin Point—As Randy Hoffman and I were standing on the beach at Wisconsin Point near the lighthouse, Randy said, "There's a Thayer's Gull." Closer inspection revealed two very similar appearing immature gulls standing on the beach. Size was almost identical, as were the bills which were the same size, yellowish-colored with dark tips. One bird appeared slightly lighter in color at rest, especially in the wingtips. This bird also had dark eyes, although I do not remember looking at the eyes of the other bird. When both birds flew, the lighter-colored bird had noticeably lighter-colored wings and wingtips. Both birds were fairly tame and soon ventured to the same resting area. Down the beach about 200 yards was a flock of several Ruddy Turnstones, Sanderlings, Red Knots, and Black-bellied Plovers. When we returned to the breakwall by the lighthouse the two gulls were still present. The lighter-colored Thayer's Gull could easily be found, in a flock of approximately 10 Ring-billed and

Herring Gulls.—*Mark S. Peterson, Box 53, Caroline, WI 54928.*

LESSER BLACK-BACKED GULL

5 April 1992, Sheboygan County, North Point—Probably a second winter-into-second summer bird; eye dark, but no dark feathering around it. Bill mostly black, but yellow showing at tip, base, and culmen. Legs yellow. Upper back very dark gray, coverts mottled with lighter tones. Chevron-like spotting on flanks and up onto breast. About 2 inches longer than Ring-billed in direct comparison. In flight, wings appeared uniformly dark gray, with black tips with no mirrors.—*Brian Boldt.*

ICELAND GULL

13 March 1992, Milwaukee County, South Shore Yacht Club—While scanning the many gulls along the pier, I noticed a pair of snow-white wingtips sticking out from behind a Ring-billed. The Ring-billed politely moved after a short while and I observed what at first appeared to be an all white gull. On closer inspection, the back, scapulars, and lesser coverts were very light gray. The rest of the folded wings were irregularly spotted with tan to gray blotches. As noted before, the primaries were clean white, and projected a good 1 1/2 inches past the tail. The head was small and rounded. The legs were pink, the bill a very dull pink with a black tip. The eye was dark. There was no streaking on the head. In flight, I got the impression of very light brown "crescents" formed by the tips of the wing coverts. Several of the secondaries and perhaps a few of the innermost primaries appeared to be light brown near the tips. Overall there was a very sloppy appearance to the upper side of the bird except for a clean, light gray triangle formed by the back and scapulars. The tail had a 1/2–3/4 inch wide light brown band, which, although light, was easily the darkest feature on this bird. The band was broken on the 1 or 2 innermost tail feathers, which seemed all white. Overall size was quite small, not much bigger than the Ring-billeds. This bird seemed particularly aggressive, several times chasing Herrings around the yacht club. At one point, it made a north to south flight about 6 ft above the water for approximately 75 yards, suddenly dropping down on each coot it saw. The coots would duck or splash aside, trying to avoid the gull. It seemed to have singled out the coots, for it changed course several times to reach the next coot, and passed by several scaup and Mallards.—*Brian Boldt.*

14 March 1992, Milwaukee County, Milwaukee River—I first noticed the bird in flight; it was an adult. Over the course of the 20 minutes it landed twice, once on the ice and once in the water. At all other times it was flying around in circles with about 100 other gulls, mostly Ring-billeds, but some Herrings, and 1 immature Glaucous. The mantle was noticeably lighter than those of the Ring-billeds. It was appreciably larger than the Ring-billeds in flight, and near to the size of the Herrings. It was noticeably smaller than the Glaucous, as a direct comparison was possible when it stood on the ice. The eye appeared dark, the bill was yellow with red gonydeal spot, and the legs were pink. From underneath, the primaries were translucent, nothing like the light gray of a Thayer's. At first glance I thought the primaries were completely white on top, but as the observation progressed I noticed several times 2 very faint dark lines on the 2 outermost primaries. When the bird was on the ice, I also noticed some faint internal markings in the tips of some primaries; these markings were the same color as the mantle.—*Brian Boldt.*

14 April 1992, Milwaukee County, South Shore Park—First year Iceland Gull. Iceland Gull was slightly smaller than the Herring Gulls and significantly larger than the Ring-billed Gulls. Bill was all black and noticeably shorter and more dainty than Herring Gull. Eyes were dark colored; legs a pale pink. When in resting position, wing tips extended beyond the tail. Tail was an even tone of very pale, speckled buff color without any hint of banding. The entire body of the bird was an even tone of pale, speckled buff with no area showing any sign of a darker tone. The primaries of the wings stood out from the general body color by being pure white. This bird was active and aggressive along the beach. It repeatedly attacked Ring-billed Gulls—causing the Ring-bills to drop whatever they might have in their bills.—*Robert C. Domagalski, W140 N8508 Lilly Rd, Menomonee Falls, WI 53051.*

16 April 1992, Douglas County, Wisconsin Point—I was watching ducks near the marsh in Allouez Bay when I noticed a small whitish gull standing on a mudflat with Herring Gulls. It was creamy white/mottled all over with pure creamy white primaries. While I watched a second winter Glaucous Gull flew in, landing nearby. The size difference was obvious. Color was nearly identical. The Iceland was a much smaller, slimmer bird than the Glaucous, a bit smaller than the Herring Gulls. Its bill was proportionately slimmer with no thickening near the tip. Its head was also smaller and more rounded than the Herring and Glaucous Gulls.

This could be the same bird that was seen several times at Wisconsin Point and up the shore in Minnesota throughout much of this winter.—*Robbye Johnson, 2602 N. 28th St, Superior, WI 54880.*

17 April 1992, Chippewa County, Lake Wissota—The ice was breaking up on Lake Wissota on April 17, and an unusually large number of water birds was congregated in areas of open water and on the edges of the ice. Among the many hundreds of gulls and ducks, one white-winged gull caught my attention immediately. It was standing near other gulls on the ice in the middle of the lake about 1/2–3/4 of a mile from where I was viewing on the west shore (distance estimated later from a map), and had completely whitish wingtips, an overall pale tawny or buff-colored plumage, pale gray patches on the back and wing coverts, pink legs and feet, and a mostly dark bill that was pale at the base. The gull was noticeably smaller than nearby Herring Gulls, and had a longer-winged, more delicate structure. The combination of distance and heat waves made it impossible, even with a Questar, to see any mottling or vermiculations on the plumage, or details of bill pattern (although the bill did appear to be more than half dark, and this area did not appear to be sharply cut off from the pale base). The bird didn't move much during the 20 minutes or so of obser-

vation, so I was unable to see the tail and underwings. As the sun set and the light became increasingly poor, I finally decided to leave, hoping to return the next morning for another look. But by the next day much of the ice had disappeared, and most of the birds were gone.—*Janine Polk, 1407 Frederic, Eau Claire, WI 54701.*

GREAT BLACK-BACKED GULL

29 March 1992, Manitowoc, Two Rivers—At the Two Rivers harbor entrance on the breakwater among the numerous Herring and Ring-billed Gulls was single adult Iceland, Glaucous and Great Black-backed Gulls. The Iceland was a pale gull, smaller than the Herrings. It had a gray mantle with white head and tail and pink feet. In flight the white outer primaries could be seen. The bill was yellow with a red spot, noticeably smaller than the Glaucous bill with a more rounded, smaller head than the Glaucous. The Great Black-backed Gull was distinct. It stood out amongst all the gulls. A *large* gull with a black back and wings, pink legs, white head and tail and massive yellow bill.—*Daryl D. Tessen, 2 Pioneer Park Pl, Elgin, IL 60123.*

3 April 1992, Manitowoc, Two Rivers—As I scoped the gulls sitting on the near breakwater I saw this one very large gull among both ring-billed and Herring Gulls. This gull stood a complete head taller than the adjacent Herring Gulls, with the head of the Herring Gull coming up to only the shoulder of the larger bird. The all black bill of the bird was about twice as large as the Herring Gull and the bird had dull pink legs. The crisp black and white plumage of the mantle, and wing coverts was in a checker pattern. The primaries were black. The eye was dark with a dark smudge surrounding it. The head, neck and breast were white with blackish streaks but appeared paler than a nearby immature Herring Gull. After observing the bird for 20 minutes, when the entire flock flew I noted the almost white rump of this bird. The tail had a black band that was not completely solid. The large size, crisp plumage, and white rump eliminate the Herring Gull.—*Kay Burcar, 5136 Enchanted Valley Rd, Cross Plains, WI 53528.*

16 April 1992, Ashland County, Chequamegon Bay—As I was driving to the Head of the Bay I glanced at a flock of gulls sitting on the ice. Since this wasn't the area I expected to see the gull I was called about, I was very surprised to see a Great Black-backed Gull standing in the flock. I stopped and set up the questar scope. Since the gull was with both Herring Gulls and Ring-billed Gulls its larger size was evident. The bill was yellow with a red spot on the lower portion near the tip. The large size of the bill was apparent when compared with bill size of the other two species.

The mantle was black as were the wings (portions I could see—the bird did not fly). Head, neck and ventral areas were white. Legs were a pale color.

After watching the bird for 10 minutes I continued to the spot where a Great Black-backed Gull was seen earlier. My friend was there and pointed out a second Great Black-backed Gull. It was resting in a flock of herring and Ring-billed Gulls. Its size was larger than either of the other species. It kept its head under its wing the entire time

we watched it but because of its size and black dorsal coloring I was sure it was the second Great Black-backed Gull to be seen in the area. These were the first I have ever recorded in this area.—*Richard L. Verch, Biology Dept., Northland College, Ashland, WI 54806.*

23 April 1992, Kewaunee County, Kewaunee Impoundment—Having just seen two Whimbrels, Brian Boldt and I walked to the north side of the impoundment to find more favorable light. While scoping with the sun at a better angle, I located a large dark mantled gull. This bird was fairly stocky and when standing it was noticeably taller than the surrounding Herring Gulls. The head was large and quite flat. The massive bill was pale yellow with a large black ring. Legs were pale pink. The most striking feature of this bird was its rather unique plumage. The scapulars were dark brown and the secondary coverts and tertials were black. Separating these dark colors was a band of white feathering which gave this gull a three-toned back. The tips of the primaries were black as was a prominent tail band. This plumage seems to indicate a 2nd summer Great Black-backed Gull.—*Mark Korducki, 4410 So. 21st Street, Milwaukee, WI 53221.*

NORTHERN HAWK-OWL

1 January–4 March 1992, Ashland County, Glidden—On January 15 I received a report from Chequamegon Forest Engineer Art Johnson of a Hawk Owl he had been seeing from the highway since January 1st. On my 2nd attempt, January 22, I located the owl perched on top of an aspen tree. Bird was seen by me 3 times a week throughout January, February, and early March. The bird was first seen by me on January 22. I looked at a bird about crow-size, with a long tail and large head, facing away and flicking its tail like a kestrel. Binocs revealed a bird with a black back with white spots, large head and a long tail. The bird was perched forward at the top of an aspen tree. When the bird's head turned toward me I noticed large yellow eyes and a yellow bill with white stripes along the top of the head. After looking at Peterson's I felt the face was greyer and the sideburns were wider than his. On January 24 the owl was perched at the top of an aspen tree next to a crossroad off Highway 13 and I was able to photograph the owl and see the breast and belly-white streaked with black. It also had a long tail and was unafraid of your approach. Three times a week I visited the owl and it was never more than 50 feet away from its original perch, always at the top of an aspen tree over-looking a snow-covered field. My last sighting was March 3rd. Forest Service biologist Dean Granholm saw the owl March 4th. Subsequent visits twice a week have failed to see the owl.—*Michael Spreeman, 722 Atwood Avenue, Park Falls, WI 54552.*

CHUCK-WILL'S-WIDOW

18 May 1992, Oconto County, northwest of Hintz—When we parked the car off County H, we could hear Whippoor-wills in the near woods. After several minutes, we faintly heard two "will's-widow" calls further to the north. This was at 8:55 P.M. Because the Chuck-will's-widow calls were so faint and distant, we decided to walk further into the woods to get closer to the Chuck-will's-widow. Just at that

time, the bird began to call from the woods quite near us. We then clear heard the "will's-widow" call repeated time after time.—*Robert C. Domagalski, W140 N8508 Lilly Rd, Menomonee Falls, WI 53051.*

VERMILLION FLYCATCHER

11 May 1992, Waukesha County, Muskego—An orange-red bird, smaller than a cardinal, a little larger than a House Finch. It had a black stripe from eye extending into back. The bill was dark and thin and pointed. The breast and head was red and a little red extended on the back rump area. The overall shape and size of the bird reminded me of a flycatcher. The wings and upper back were blackish (not deep black). The bird spent a lot of time in our maple trees—flying from one to the next. It would leave our yard and return within a short period of time. Almost every hour that I was watching for it, it was around. The tail was held down as it sat in a tree. It would dart around the tree and then stop; move to another tree and so on.—*Mary Jo Welnak, W147 S6960 Durham Dr, Muskego, WI 53150.*

TREE SWALLOW

5 March 1992, Dodge County, Rock River—Getting out of the car I watched for about a minute when the bird again flew past the spot—and could be seen again and again over the next 10 minutes. The bird came within 100 feet of me—giving chances of excellent looks. All white undersides and throat; back a glossy dark blue-green; long and pointed wings, tail slightly notched. Bird was definitely an adult male Tree Swallow. Only one bird was seen. Gnat-like insects were abundant all morning along the Rock River.

I write this not because the Tree Swallow is unusual in Wisconsin—but because this is an exceptionally early sighting. According to Robbins (1991), the only record of an earlier sighting was March 2, 1973.—*Robert C. Domagalski, W140 N8508 Lilly Rd, Menomonee Falls, WI 53051.*

BLACK-BILLED MAGPIE

2 May 1992, Columbia County, Schoeneberg Marsh—Upon arriving at the bend in the road at Schoeneberg's Marsh in Columbia Co. to look for a Cinnamon Teal which had been reported there several days earlier, I almost immediately noticed a fairly large bird flying with the wind (from northwest to southeast) just approaching the road ahead of me. What caught my eye was the extremely long tail, obvious even without binoculars. Using my binoculars, I noted the following field marks as the bird continued to fly across the road and disappeared in the distance behind a wood lot. The tail appeared longer than the body, pointed, and dark in color (lighting only permitted some light/dark contrasts). While flying over the road ahead of me, I noted the dark, wide wings were crossed with broad white wing stripes, quite contrasting in flight. The flight was strong and steady. I could not see the back until the bird was in the distance, when two white patches were seen on the sides of the back. The undersides were two tone, blackish on the breast and whitish on the belly. The only size comparison available was with a Red-tailed Hawk seen momentarily in the same field of view. The magpie was a smaller bird,

but of about the same length (when including tail). No sound was given. This sighting coincided with a rash of unusual bird observations that weekend, including a Summer Tanager I located the day before in Milwaukee.—*Dennis K. Gustafson, 15440 Linfield Lane, New Berlin, WI 53151.*

CAROLINA WREN

21 March 1992, Iowa County, Gov. Dodge Park—About 10:30 A.M. I heard the three syllable, three phrase call of this bird while observing many Dark-eyed Juncos, Fox Sparrows, Song Sparrows, and Tree Sparrows at the boat landing of Twin Lake at Governor Dodge State Park in Iowa Co. I briefly saw the bird fly and noted the buffy breast, long white eye stripe and long wren type tail. I was within 30 feet of the bird. The weather was windy with snow falling.—*Kay Burcar, 5136 Enchanted Valley Rd, Cross Plains, WI 53528.*

NORTHERN MOCKINGBIRD

3 April 1992, Winnebago County, Oshkosh—I saw this bird at 5:30 A.M. on 4-3 in the church parking lot in Oshkosh following the hot line tip noting its presence. The bird sat on lower branches about two feet from the ground several times for about five minutes so allowed a perfect view from ten to fifteen feet in distance. I noted the long gray tail which the bird flicked both sideways and up and down. The black bill was thin and sharp. The head and upper breast were gray, while the throat and belly was whitish. The prominent wing bars were observed and the white wing patch and tail edges were noted when the bird flew. The bird's eye had a light iris with a dark pupil. Some of its song was heard but no mimic songs were noted. The bird actively defended a crab apple tree where it fed from several robins' encroachment. Total viewing time was 25 minutes with the bird in view constantly. The lack of a black face mask, the large white wing patches in flight, and thin, sharp bill eliminate a shrike.—*Kay Burcar, 5136 Enchanted Valley Rd, Cross Plains, WI 53528.*

YELLOW-THROATED WARBLER

6 May 1992, Manitowoc County, Silver Creek Park—During an otherwise slow day of birding on my noon walk in Silver Creek Park, I happened upon an Ash tree that had 7 or 8 Myrtle Warblers actively feeding and moving about. The tree was still bare as trees in the lake shore area leaf out slowly. Because it was running late, I almost passed off the entire group of warblers as Myrtles, but stopped briefly to enjoy the few warblers that had appeared in the park area that day. To my surprise, and obvious delight, the first bird I looked at was not a Myrtle, but the Yellow-throated Warbler. I had seen large numbers of these birds in Alabama and South Carolina in the summer of 1972, but had not found one in Wisconsin. The canary yellow throat was bordered by black that extended from the eye to the streaking on the sides. The black area around the eye was outlined by white above the eye (supercillary) and behind the eye in the oricular area. The black around the eye created an upside down triangular pattern that extended and was continuous with the streaking on the sides. The top of the head, nape and back were bluish gray quite similar to the Myrtles in the immediate area. The breast and belly were white, with the yellow extending as a pointed bib into the breast area. The wing bars on the darker bluish wings were evident, and the tail had obvious spots that were easily seen when the bird flew from branch to branch while feeding. Although I was now late for class, I continued to observe the bird for about 10 minutes at distances of between 20 to 30 feet with 10×40 binocs. The lighting was excellent as it was over my left shoulder at angles up to 90 degrees. The Myrtles and Yellow-throated Warbler remained in the Ash tree the entire time moving only from side to side. At one point, the Yellow-throated stopped to vocalize, but it was almost inaudible even at the short distance, and its characteristic song was not distinguished.—*Charles Sontag, 801 N. 4th Street, Manitowoc, WI 54220.*

23 May 1992, Grant County, Wyalusing Park—While searching for Kentucky Warblers, etc. along the beginning of the Long Valley Road (by the pines) a warbler suddenly flew into a tree across from the pines. A quick look revealed a Yellow-throated Warbler. It remained in the tree for 1–2 minutes until a Chipping Sparrow chased it. It flew across the ravine into the trees where it commenced singing. Easily noted was the gray back, white wing bars (2), black stripes on the side of the breast and belly, yellow throat, with black extending from eyes down on to black stripes, and white eye stripe.—*Daryl Tessen, 2 Pioneer Park Pl, Elgin, IL 60123.*

26 May 1992, Sauk County, Cedarburg Bog—As I have no previous experience with this species, I did not immediately recognize the song. I listened to it repeated several times over the next perhaps, two minutes, and wrote down my interpretation of the song so that I could make an identification later after reviewing taped songs of warbler (Peterson's and Cornell tapes). The first time I heard the recorded Yellow-throated Warbler's song I believed very strongly that this is the bird that I heard. I still feel this way after many more playings of the above tapes. The following is my written rendition of this song as taken from my field notes, made at the time the song was heard: "tsu-tsu-tsu-tsu-tsu tsu-tsu-tsu." The first 5 syllables descended and were evenly spaced. The last 3 (sometimes only 2 were heard) were rapid and did not rise or fall. I would guess that the bird was singing from about 50 yards away, perhaps less. I had no trouble hearing the song. I never saw the bird.—*Scott Diehl, S68 W12977 Camilia Dr., Muskego, WI 53150.*

WORM-EATING WARBLER

17 May 1992, Dane County, UW Arboretum—On 5-17-92 while walking on the Madison arboretum trail near the parking lot I heard the short insect like trill of this species. The bird called six times. I saw White-throated Sparrows along the ground, but wasn't able to see this bird. Again on 5-18-92 I heard the insect like buzz of very short duration while walking along the Willow Springs Trail west of the spring. Ellen Hanson and Dave Fallow also heard the call and agreed on the identification of this species.—*Kay Burcar, 5136 Enchanted Valley Rd, Cross Plains, WI 53528.*

SHARP-TAILED SPARROW

23 May 1992, Oconto County, Oconto Marsh—The bird was not seen. But 4 of us on the Dike heard this insect-like call about 15 feet away from a clump of grass in the marsh. We listened for about 1–2 min. and heard this call several times. I have heard this before in North Dakota and immediately recognized this. Within 15 minutes I played the tape of this bird and we all agreed we had heard a Sharp-tailed Sparrow. We tried to see the bird but it remained low in the grasses and stopped calling after we tried to "pish" the bird out.—*Bob Mead.*

RUSTY BLACKBIRD

10 May 1992, Milwaukee County, Kleztch Park—I first saw the light yellowish eye of this blackbird, then had to change positions because of the many leaves to observe the light barring on the breast. The bill was long and pointed but more delicate than that of a grackle. The tail was straight on the end unlike the diagonal of the grackle. The call which resembles the creaking of a rusty hinge confirmed the identification. The yellowish eye, and light barring eliminates the Brewer's Blackbird, the smaller, and straight tail eliminates the grackle.—*Kay Burcar, 5136 Enchanted Valley Rd, Cross Plains, WI 53528.*

Laughing Gulls *by Frank Mittelstadt.*

ABOUT THE AUTHORS AND ARTISTS

Jim Frank has been one of WSO's most active contributors to Seasonal Field-Notes. He now assists WSO by compiling and summarizing the annual May Day Counts and Big Day Counts. He is a veterinarian in Milwaukee with an interest in avian medicine.

Robert W. Howe is a Professor of Natural and Applied Sciences at UW-Green Bay; he is also Chair of WSO's Research Committee.

Frank Mittelstadt is a native of Beaver Dam. Winner of the 1993 Wisconsin Waterfowl Stamp, 1992 Wisconsin Trout Stamp and Great Lakes Salmon and Trout Stamp competitions, he is represented by Eagle Publishing, Beaver Dam, WI 53916.

Michael J. Mossman is a nongame biologist with the Wisconsin DNR's Bureau of Research. He has a M.S. degree in Wildlife Ecology from UW-Madison. He is a frequent contributor to *The Passenger Pigeon* and other WSO activities.

Robert Rolley is a research biologist with the Wisconsin DNR's Bureau of Research. He has his M.S. in Wildlife Ecology from the University of Wisconsin-Madison and his Ph.D. from the University of Oklahoma. He is currently coordinating The Wisconsin Checklist Project.

Allen K. Shea is our current President and the Spring Field-Note compiler. He is the Assistant to the Director of the DNR's Bureau of Water Resources. He has his M.S. degree in Water Resources Management from the UW-Madison's Institute for Environmental Studies.

Stanley A. Temple is Editor of *The Passenger Pigeon* and a Professor of Wildlife Ecology at the UW-Madison. He has authored several WSO publications and has received WSO's Golden Passenger Pigeon Award.

William J. Vander Zouwen is a wildlife biologist with the Wisconsin DNR's Bureau of Wildlife Management where he works on upland game species. He has his M.S. in Wildlife Ecology from the University of Wisconsin-Madison.

INDEX TO VOLUME 54

A

Abel, Becky, Snapping Turtle Attacks on Trumpeter Swan Cygnets in Wisconsin, 209–213; Abel, Becky, and Ilene Grossman, Observations of a Lead Poisoned Trumpeter Swan, 215–219

Acadian Flycatcher, 43–48, 91, 110, 134, 141, 143, 144, 163, 263, 319, 343

Alder Flycatcher, 141, 163, 263, 319, 343

American Avocet, 154, 159, 175, 233, 239, 315

American Bittern, 85, 131, 139, 155, 260, 262, 309, 311, 336, 339

American Black Duck, 8–14, 79, 85, 128, 139, 156, 225, 262, 312, 336, 340

American Coot, 15, 85, 86, 128, 131–132, 140, 159, 180, 227, 262, 269, 271, 279, 293, 315, 337, 340

American Crow, 9–14, 80, 105, 129, 131–134, 136, 141, 164, 224, 233, 247–249, 264, 299, 320, 338, 341

American Goldfinch, 9–14, 95, 101, 130, 131, 143, 148, 171, 231, 261, 265, 326, 339, 342

American Kestrel, 9–14, 16, 95, 128, 131, 139, 150, 158, 224, 226, 246, 261, 262, 314, 337, 340

American Redstart, 130, 132, 142, 144, 167, 265, 323, 339, 342

American Robin, 9–14, 18, 81, 129, 131, 132, 134, 141, 151, 165, 224, 229, 264, 299, 321, 338, 341

American Swallow-tailed Kite, 80

American Tree Sparrow, 9–14, 18, 130, 142, 168, 223, 229, 265, 324, 343

American White Pelican, 79, 86, 87, 154, 155, 311, 327–329, 342

American Wigeon, 8, 15, 87, 128, 139, 156, 173, 225, 262, 270–272, 282–284, 288, 289, 337, 340, 351, 352

American Woodcock, 67, 80, 86, 140, 160, 260, 263, 300, 317, 337, 340

B

Baird's Sandpiper, 89, 140, 160, 263, 316, 329, 330, 333, 343

Bald Eagle, 9–14, 16, 68, 71, 80, 85, 128, 131, 133, 134, 136, 139, 143, 157, 224, 226, 233, 237, 243, 262, 301, 303, 313, 337, 340

Bank Swallow, 127, 129, 132, 134, 141, 164, 264, 320, 338, 341

Barn Swallow, 129, 141, 164, 248, 260, 264, 320, 338, 341

Barred Owl, 9–14, 17, 80, 86, 97, 129, 140, 162, 183, 224, 245, 246, 263, 299, 300, 318, 337, 341

Barrett, Gabrielle V., Public Attitudes Toward Park Mallards in Stevens Point, Wisconsin, 119–123

Bay-breasted Warbler, 93, 142, 167, 264, 322, 338, 342

Baughman, Jeffrey L., "By the Wayside," 351–352

Baughman, Scott J., "By the Wayside," 347, 347–348, 352–353

Belant, Jerrold L., Pre-Migratory Territorial Activities of Common Loons on Single-Pair Lakes, 115–118; "By the Wayside," 233–234, 234–235

Bell's Vireo, 92, 110, 141, 143, 144, 166, 264, 321, 327, 331

Belted Kingfisher, 9–14, 80, 86, 127–129, 131, 132, 134, 140, 163, 224, 228, 260, 263, 319, 337, 341

Bielefeldt, John, and Robert N. Rosenfield, Acadian Flycatchers Nesting in Conifer Plantations in Southeastern Wisconsin, 43–49

Black-and-white Warbler, 93, 130, 142, 144, 167, 265, 298, 300, 302, 323, 339, 342

Black-backed Woodpecker, 15, 17, 86, 90, 154, 163, 222, 228, 301, 302, 319, 335, 343

Black-bellied Plover, 89, 159, 175, 176, 181, 263, 309, 315, 343, 358

Black-billed Cuckoo, 86, 140, 162, 263, 300, 318, 337, 341

Black-billed Magpie, 80, 310, 320, 345, 363

Black-capped Chickadee, 9–14, 100, 129, 131, 132, 141, 148, 150, 164, 224, 250, 261, 264, 320, 338, 341

Black-crowned Night-Heron, 51–53, 55, 87, 128, 139, 155, 262, 309, 311, 336, 340

Black-legged Kittiwake, 154, 161, 173, 181

Black-necked Stilt, 154, 159, 173, 174

Black Scoter, 139, 144, 157, 225, 262, 313, 330, 331, 343

Black-shouldered Kite, 345, 353

Black Tern, 80, 86, 140, 144, 162, 245, 263, 318, 337, 340

Black-throated Blue Warbler, 92, 142, 167, 264, 300, 301, 303, 322, 329, 331, 332, 338, 342

Black-throated Green Warbler, 86, 92, 130, 142, 143, 167, 264, 300, 322, 338, 342

Blackburnian Warbler, 92, 130, 142, 167, 264, 300, 301, 322, 338, 342

Blackpoll Warbler, 130, 142, 167, 264, 322, 338, 342

Blue-gray Gnatcatcher, 91, 129, 141, 143, 165, 264, 320, 338, 341

Blue Grosbeak, 142–144

Blue Jay, 9–14, 80, 129, 131, 132, 141, 148, 164, 224, 248, 249, 264, 303, 320, 338, 341

Blue-winged Teal, 86, 128, 132, 139, 156, 198, 200, 201, 262, 271, 272, 312, 337, 340, 350, 351

Blue-winged Warbler, 92, 142, 166, 264, 322, 338, 341

Bobolink, 86, 101, 143, 144, 169, 193, 260, 265, 325, 339, 342

Bohemian Waxwing, 16, 18, 141, 166, 229, 264, 321

Boldt, Brian, "By the Wayside," 173, 174–175, 180–181, 182, 241–242, 357, 357–358, 358, 358–359, 359

Bonaparte's Gull, 15, 17, 90, 96, 128, 140, 161, 177, 179, 181, 227, 263, 317, 337, 340, 356

Boreal Chickadee, 15, 91, 164, 223, 228, 264, 298, 300, 320, 335, 343

Brant, 79, 154, 155, 173, 174, 294

Brasser, David, "By the Wayside," 98; Brasser, David, and Margaret Brasser, "By the Wayside," 243

Brasser, Margaret, see Brasser, David, and Margaret Brasser

Breihan, Bill, "By the Wayside," 100–101

Brewer's Blackbird, 16, 18, 86, 130, 143, 170, 223, 230, 265, 325, 339, 342, 365
Broad-winged Hawk, 5, 85, 86, 128, 132, 133, 139, 158, 246, 262, 300, 314, 337, 340
Brown Creeper, 9–14, 17, 91, 129, 141, 143, 164, 223, 228, 264, 300, 301, 320, 338, 341
Brown-headed Cowbird, 16, 18, 130, 131, 134, 143, 170, 223, 224, 230, 265, 325, 339, 342
Brown Thrasher, 16, 81, 86, 129, 131, 132, 141, 165, 229, 260, 264, 321, 338, 341
Buff-breasted Sandpiper, 154, 160, 327, 328
Bufflehead, 15, 88, 128, 139, 157, 225, 262, 270–273, 281, 283, 284, 285, 286, 287, 293, 313, 337, 340
Burcar, Kay, "By the Wayside," 97–98, 98, 99–100, 173–174, 175–176, 176, 180, 244, 347, 348, 348–349, 350, 351, 352, 354, 354–355, 355–356, 357, 360–361, 363, 363–364, 365

C

Canada Goose, 9–14, 79, 128, 131, 132, 139, 155, 173, 174, 204, 212, 224, 261, 262, 271, 312, 336, 340, 348, 349
Canada Warbler, 93, 130, 142, 143, 168, 265, 300, 323, 339, 342
Canvasback, 15, 87, 128, 139, 156, 225, 262, 270–273, 281, 284–287, 291, 293, 294, 313, 329–332, 337, 340, 350
Cape May Warbler, 92, 130, 142, 167, 264, 322, 338, 341
Carolina Wren, 15, 17, 86, 91, 154, 164, 222, 228, 233, 249, 320, 331, 343, 345, 363
Caspian Tern, 86, 129, 140, 144, 161, 263, 318, 337, 340
Cattle Egret, 87, 155, 262, 311, 328–330, 332, 342
Cedar Waxwing, 9–14, 18, 129, 131, 132, 141, 166, 224, 229, 264, 301, 321, 338, 341
Cerulean Warbler, 93, 110, 142–144, 167, 264, 323, 339, 342
Chestnut-sided Warbler, 130, 142, 143, 167, 264, 298, 300, 322, 338, 341
Chimney Swift, 129, 140, 162, 263, 318, 337, 341
Chipping Sparrow, 16, 18, 100, 130, 132, 142, 168, 229, 265, 324, 339, 342, 364
Chuck-will's-widow, 86, 90, 95, 97, 98, 345, 362
Cinnamon Teal, 139, 144, 310, 312, 335, 343, 345, 350, 351, 363
Clark's Nutcracker, 248
Clay-colored Sparrow, 142, 168, 265, 324, 339, 342
Cliff Swallow, 86, 128, 129, 134, 141, 164, 264, 320, 338, 341
Common Barn-Owl, 154, 162, 263
Common Black-headed Gull, 86, 90, 95, 96
Common Goldeneye, 8–14, 128, 131, 139, 157, 225, 262, 272, 273, 281, 285, 313, 332, 337, 340
Common Grackle, 9–14, 18, 130, 131, 134, 143, 148, 170, 223, 224, 230, 260, 265, 325, 339, 342
Common Loon, 15, 16, 19–23, 26–29, 79, 87, 115–118, 128, 131, 134, 139, 154, 224, 233–235, 262, 269, 271, 310, 336, 339, 345, 346
Common Merganser, 8–14, 88, 128, 131, 139, 157, 198, 225, 262, 271, 273, 313, 329, 330, 337, 340
Common Moorhen, 89, 159, 262, 315, 343
Common Nighthawk, 86, 129, 132, 140, 162, 260, 263, 318, 337, 341
Common Raven, 9–14, 80, 91, 164, 228, 248, 249, 264, 320, 338, 341
Common Redpoll, 9–14, 18, 130, 143, 150, 170, 222, 231, 250, 265, 325, 344

Common Snipe, 15, 17, 67, 86, 140, 160, 227, 263, 317, 337, 340
Common Tern, 80, 86, 129, 161, 245, 263, 318, 337, 340
Common Yellowthroat, 81, 130, 131, 142, 168, 193, 265, 323, 339, 342
Connecticut Warbler, 93, 142, 168, 265, 323, 327, 329–331, 333, 339, 342
Cooper's Hawk, 9–14, 16, 85, 128, 131, 132, 133, 134, 139, 144, 157, 224, 226, 261, 262, 309, 314, 337, 340
Cowart, Bill, "By the Wayside," 174, 177, 181, 182
Craven, Scott R., Most Frequently Asked Questions About Birds, 147–152

D

Dark-eyed Junco, 9–14, 18, 94, 127, 130, 134, 143, 148, 169, 230, 265, 325, 329, 339, 342, 363
Dickcissel, 86, 93, 134, 142–144, 168, 193, 194, 265, 324, 327, 329–331
Diehl, Scott, "By the Wayside," 364–365
Domagalski, Robert C., "By the Wayside," 98, 98–99, 99, 175, 177, 179, 179–180, 242–243, 244, 350, 355, 359, 362, 362–363
Donald, Mary F., 1992 Silver Passenger Pigeon Awardees, 251–254
Double-crested Cormorant, 15, 16, 51, 52, 54, 55, 57, 79, 85, 128, 131, 134, 139, 155, 224, 262, 270, 311, 336, 339
Downy Woodpecker, 9–14, 17, 129, 131, 132, 140, 163, 224, 253, 261, 263, 319, 338, 341
Dunlin, 89, 160, 176, 239, 263, 316, 337, 340, 355, 356
Dunn, Terry Daulton, Status of the Common Loon in Wisconsin, 19–29
Dykstra, Cheryl, "By the Wayside," 237–238

E

Eared Grebe, 86, 87, 154, 311, 328, 345, 347
Eastern Bluebird, 16, 18, 81, 86, 91, 127, 129, 131, 132, 134, 141, 144, 150, 165, 223, 229, 261, 264, 302, 321, 338, 341
Eastern Kingbird, 129, 131, 132, 141, 164, 264, 319, 338, 341
Eastern Meadowlark, 16, 86, 131, 134, 143, 170, 193, 265, 325, 339, 342
Eastern Phoebe, 129, 131, 141, 150, 163, 261, 264, 319, 338, 341
Eastern Screech-Owl, 9–14, 90, 140, 150, 162, 227, 263, 318, 343
Eastern Wood-Pewee, 141, 163, 263, 319, 338, 341
Edrop, Arthur J.M., "By the Wayside," 250
Eurasian Tree Sparrow, 231
Eurasian Wigeon, 345, 351, 352
European Starling, 9–14, 129, 131, 132, 134, 141, 148, 150, 166, 229, 248, 264, 321, 338, 341
Evening Grosbeak, 9–14, 18, 86, 130, 143, 148, 150, 171, 231, 260, 265, 301, 326–329, 339, 342

F

Field Sparrow, 16, 18, 86, 94, 130–132, 142, 144, 168, 193, 195, 265, 324, 339, 342
Forster's Tern, 67, 86, 140, 143, 161, 263, 318, 337, 340
Fox Sparrow, 16, 18, 130, 142, 169, 223, 229, 261, 265, 324, 344, 363
Frank, James C., "By the Wayside," 174, 175, 182–

183, 350; Big Day Counts: 1992, 327–333; May Day Counts: 1992, 335–344

Franklin's Gull, 90, 161, 179, 180, 263, 309, 317, 330, 343, 357

G

Gadwall, 15, 87, 128, 131, 139, 156, 225, 262, 270–272, 281–284, 288, 289, 312, 337, 340

Glaucous Gull, 15, 17, 129, 161, 180, 182, 227, 242, 261, 263, 317, 343, 357, 359, 360

Glossy Ibis, 139, 144

Glueckert, Kevin, "By the Wayside," 181

Golden-crowned Kinglet, 9–14, 17, 86, 91, 129, 141, 165, 223, 229, 264, 320, 343

Golden Eagle, 15, 16, 154, 158, 226, 314

Golden-winged Warbler, 86, 142, 166, 264, 298, 300, 322, 338, 341

Grasshopper Sparrow, 86, 142, 144, 169, 192–195, 265, 310, 324, 339, 342

Gray Catbird, 16, 18, 129, 131, 132, 141, 165, 229, 264, 321, 338, 341

Gray-cheeked Thrush, 129, 141, 165, 260, 264, 321, 338, 341

Gray Jay, 15, 17, 91, 164, 223, 228, 248, 264, 298, 300, 302, 320, 329, 343

Gray Partridge, 15, 17, 140, 158, 226, 262, 314, 333, 343

Great Black-backed Gull, 3, 5, 17, 154, 161, 173, 180, 181, 227, 233, 242, 243, 310, 317, 327, 330, 345, 360–362, 361

Great Blue Heron, 9–14, 17, 51–55, 57, 79, 86, 128, 131, 134, 139, 155, 174, 222, 224, 261, 262, 309, 311, 336, 340, 347

Great Crested Flycatcher, 129, 131, 163, 338, 341

Great Egret, 51–58, 87, 128, 139, 143, 155, 262, 309, 311, 336, 340, 347

Great Gray Owl, 86, 90, 95, 97, 222, 228, 233, 246, 310, 318

Great Horned Owl, 9–14, 17, 140, 162, 224, 263, 299, 301, 318, 337, 341

Greater Prairie-Chicken, 15, 80, 88, 158, 226, 262, 314, 343

Greater Scaup, 15, 88, 128, 139, 156, 225, 262, 270, 284, 313, 327, 329, 331, 332, 337, 340

Greater White-fronted Goose, 154, 155, 312, 348

Greater Yellowlegs, 89, 128, 140, 159, 263, 315, 337, 340

Green, Robert, "By the Wayside," 244

Green-backed Heron, 86, 126–128, 131, 132, 134, 139, 155, 262, 311, 336, 340

Green-winged Teal, 16, 80, 85, 128, 139, 156, 198, 225, 233, 236, 237, 261, 262, 271, 272, 283, 312, 336, 340

Grossman, Ilene, see Abel, Becky, and Ilene Grossman

Gustafson, Dennis K., "By the Wayside," 243, 363

Gyrfalcon, 140, 144, 226, 238, 239, 310, 314

H

Hairy Woodpecker, 9–14, 17, 86, 101, 129, 131, 140, 163, 224, 253, 263, 319, 338, 341

Hale, James, and Sam Robbins, "By the Wayside," 349–350

Hale, Karen Etter, "By the Wayside," 350–351

Harlequin Duck, 15, 16, 154, 156, 225, 313, 330, 331, 333, 345, 352

Harris' Sparrow, 130, 132, 144, 154, 169, 265, 324, 333, 344

Hartman, Lisa M., see Mossman, Michael J., and Lisa A. Hartman

Henslow's Sparrow, 94, 142, 144, 169, 192–195, 260, 265, 310, 324, 327, 329, 330, 331, 332, 339, 342

Hermit Thrush, 16, 86, 129, 141, 165, 229, 248, 264, 298–300, 321, 338, 341

Herring Gull, 9–14, 17, 80, 86, 97, 129, 140, 161, 177, 178–181, 183, 224, 227, 240–244, 263, 317, 337, 340, 357–361

Hilsenhoff, William L., The 1991 Wisconsin Christmas Bird Counts, 3–18

Hoary Redpoll, 16, 18, 231, 326

Hooded Merganser, 15, 80, 85, 128, 139, 143, 157, 198, 225, 262, 270, 271, 273, 285, 287, 300, 301, 302, 313, 337, 340

Hooded Warbler, 93, 110, 142–144, 265, 323, 329, 333, 343

Horned Grebe, 128, 139, 154, 262, 270, 311, 331, 332, 342, 347

Horned Lark, 9–14, 18, 141, 164, 224, 228, 264, 319, 338, 341

House Finch, 9–14, 86, 94, 130, 131, 143, 149, 151, 170, 223, 230, 265, 323, 325, 339, 342, 362

House Sparrow, 9–14, 130–132, 143, 148, 150, 171, 231, 247, 249, 265, 326, 339, 342

House Wren, 129, 131, 132, 141, 150, 164, 229, 264, 299, 320, 338, 341

Howe, Robert W., Research Opportunities for Part-Time Ornithologists, 107–114; Howe, Robert W., Stanley A. Temple and Michael J. Mossman, Forest Management and Birds in Northern Wisconsin, 297–305

Hudsonian Godwit, 159, 263, 316, 328–331, 333, 343

Hughes, Robert, "By the Wayside," 178, 240

I

Iceland Gull, 86, 90, 95, 96, 154, 161, 173, 180, 182, 227, 233, 242, 310, 317, 345, 357–359

Indigo Bunting, 130–132, 134, 142, 168, 265, 324, 339, 342

Ivory Gull, 154, 161, 173, 182, 222, 227, 233, 244

J

Johnson, Robbye J., "By the Wayside," 181–182, 183, 242, 359–360

K

Kentucky Warbler, 93, 142, 143, 265, 323, 327, 330, 343, 364

Killdeer, 17, 67, 86, 128, 134, 140, 159, 224, 227, 260, 263, 315, 337, 340, 355

King Rail, 88, 140, 144, 154, 158, 309, 315, 327, 330–332, 343, 345, 354

Kirtland's Warbler, 86, 93

Korducki, Mark, "By the Wayside," 176–177, 177–178, 238–239, 240, 241, 356–357, 361

Krysiak, Daniel E., "By the Wayside," 353

L

Lange, Kenneth I., The Winter Season: 1991–92, 221–231

Lapland Longspur, 16, 18, 143, 169, 223, 230, 265, 325, 330, 331, 333, 344

Lark Bunting, 86, 94, 95, 100–102, 101, 142, 144

Lark Sparrow, 94, 169, 265, 324, 327, 329–331, 344

Laughing Gull, 86, 90, 154, 161, 173, 179, 180, 309, 310, 317, 345, 356

Le Conte's Sparrow, 265, 327–332, 339, 342

Least Bittern, 85, 128, 139, 144, 155, 262, 309, 311, 336, 339

Least Flycatcher, 129, 131, 141, 163, 263, 300, 319, 338, 341

Least Sandpiper, 89, 128, 140, 160, 261, 263, 316, 337, 340

Least Tern, 233, 244

Lesser Black-backed Gull, 227, 233, 242, 243, 310, 317, 345, 358

Lesser Golden-Plover, 159, 263, 309, 315, 328, 330–332, 343

Lesser Scaup, 8, 15, 88, 128, 139, 156, 225, 262, 270, 284, 294, 313, 337, 340

Lesser Yellowlegs, 89, 140, 159, 263, 315, 337, 340

Lincoln's Sparrow, 3, 5, 94, 130, 143, 169, 230, 265, 300, 324, 339, 342

Little Blue Heron, 139, 144, 310, 311, 327, 332, 345, 347

Little Gull, 86, 90, 154, 161, 309, 317

Loggerhead Shrike, 5, 92, 154, 166, 229, 233, 249, 250, 264, 321, 327, 330, 335, 343

Long, Charles A., and Claudine F. Long, Some Effects of Land Use on Avian Diversity in a Wisconsin's Oak-Pine Savanna and Riparian Forest, 125–136

Long, Claudine F., see Long, Charles A., and Claudine F. Long

Long-billed Dowitcher, 90, 160, 263, 317, 327, 330–332

Long-eared Owl, 15, 17, 90, 140, 162, 228, 263, 318, 327–329, 331, 343

Louisiana Waterthrush, 93, 142, 143, 168, 265, 323, 327–332, 343

M

Magnolia Warbler, 92, 130, 142, 167, 264, 322, 338, 341

Mahn, Carlton, "By the Wayside," 249

Mallard, 8–14, 80, 95, 119, 122, 123, 128, 131, 132, 134, 139, 156, 173, 198, 200, 201, 207, 225, 262, 270–274, 279, 280, 281–284, 288, 293, 294, 312, 336, 340, 348, 352, 359

Marbled Godwit, 263, 316, 328, 329, 332

Marks, Jim B., "By the Wayside," 238, 239

Marsh Wren, 3, 5, 15, 91, 129, 141, 165, 229, 264, 320, 338, 341

McCarthy, Mary M., see C. Edward Miller and Mary M. McCarthy

Mead, Bob, "By the Wayside," 365

Merlin, 15, 16, 80, 88, 128, 139, 158, 226, 261, 262, 314, 329, 332, 343

Mew Gull, 227, 233, 239, 240

Miller, C. Edward and Mary M. McCarthy, "By the Wayside," 345–346

Mossman, Michael J., H. R. Schoolcraft and Natural History on the Western Frontier, Part 2: The 1820 Expedition, 59–84; Mossman, Michael J., and Lisa M. Hartman, Turkey Vulture Nest Records from Wisconsin, 31–41; see Howe, Robert W., Stanley A. Temple and Michael J. Mossman

Mourning Dove, 9–14, 17, 80, 105, 129, 131, 132, 134, 140, 148, 162, 227, 250, 261, 263, 318, 337, 340

Mourning Warbler, 93, 130, 142, 143, 168, 265, 298, 300, 323, 339, 342

Mute Swan, 15, 16, 87, 128, 131, 132, 139, 155, 209, 210, 212, 213, 215, 224, 262, 312, 336, 340

N

Nashville Warbler, 92, 130, 142, 143, 166, 264, 298, 300, 322, 335, 338, 341

Nauertz, Scot T., Peck-Order Formation in Decoy-Reared Trumpeter Swans, 203–207

Northern Bobwhite, 15, 17, 88, 131, 132, 140, 158, 222, 227, 262, 314, 343

Northern Cardinal, 9–14, 93, 130, 132, 134, 142, 148, 151, 168, 229, 261, 265, 323, 339, 342

Northern Flicker, 9–14, 17, 86, 129, 131, 134, 141, 163, 223, 228, 263, 319, 338, 341

Northern Goshawk, 9–14, 16, 88, 128, 157, 222, 223, 226, 261, 262, 300, 314, 329, 343

Northern Harrier, 9–14, 16, 128, 139, 144, 157, 193, 222, 224, 226, 248, 261, 262, 302, 309, 313, 337, 340, 353

Northern Hawk-Owl, 154, 162, 173, 183, 222, 228, 233, 243, 245, 246, 310, 318, 345, 361

Northern Mockingbird, 16, 64, 81, 86, 92, 141, 143, 144, 264, 321, 345, 363

Northern Oriole, 86, 130–132, 143, 151, 170, 265, 325, 339, 342

Northern Parula, 86, 142, 166, 264, 301, 303, 322, 338, 341

Northern Pintail, 15, 87, 139, 156, 225, 262, 271, 272, 312, 336, 340

Northern Rough-winged Swallow, 127, 129, 134, 141, 164, 338, 341

Northern Saw-whet Owl, 15, 17, 90, 129, 140, 162, 228, 263, 300, 318, 329, 343

Northern Shoveler, 15, 87, 128, 139, 156, 225, 262, 271, 272, 283, 312, 337, 340, 349, 352

Northern Shrike, 9–14, 18, 141, 166, 223, 229, 264, 321

Northern Waterthrush, 93, 130, 142, 167, 265, 301, 323, 335, 339, 342

O

Oldsquaw, 8, 15, 16, 86, 88, 156, 225, 262, 270, 313, 331, 332

Olive-sided Flycatcher, 91, 129, 141, 163, 263, 319, 343

Orange-crowned Warbler, 142, 166, 264, 308, 322, 327, 329, 333, 343

Orchard Oriole, 94, 144, 170, 265, 325, 327, 328, 330–332, 344

Osprey, 5, 88, 128, 131–134, 139, 143, 157, 262, 303, 313, 337, 340

Ovenbird, 86, 130, 142, 167, 265, 298, 300, 323, 339, 342

P

Palm Warbler, 93, 130, 142, 167, 264, 300, 302, 308, 322, 338, 342

Parasitic Jaeger, 154, 161, 173, 177, 178

Pectoral Sandpiper, 89, 128, 140, 160, 176, 263, 316, 337, 340

Peregrine Falcon, 5, 15, 16, 80, 88, 139, 143, 158, 226, 238, 262, 314, 315, 330–333

Peterson, Mark S., The Fall Season: 1991, 153–171; "By the Wayside," 242, 358

Philadelphia Vireo, 86, 92, 142, 166, 264, 308, 322, 343

Pied-billed Grebe, 15, 85, 128, 131, 139, 154, 224, 262, 270, 311, 336, 339

Pileated Woodpecker, 9–14, 17, 86, 132, 141, 144, 163, 224, 261, 263, 300, 301, 302, 319, 338, 341

Pine Grosbeak, 16, 18, 130, 143, 170, 222, 230, 265, 325

Pine Siskin, 9–14, 18, 94, 130, 132, 143, 150, 170, 231, 265, 326, 328, 329, 331, 339, 342

Pine Warbler, 93, 98, 130, 142, 167, 264, 301, 322, 327, 329, 328–330, 332, 338, 342

Piping Plover, 67, 89, 310, 315, 335, 343, 345, 355

Polk, Janine, "By the Wayside," 178–179, 360

Prairie Warbler, 142, 322, 327, 330

Prothonotary Warbler, 81, 93, 142, 167, 265, 323, 327, 329, 343

Purple Finch, 9–14, 94, 130, 143, 148, 170, 230, 265, 298, 300, 325, 339, 342

Purple Martin, 86, 129, 131, 132, 141, 150, 164, 260, 264, 319, 338, 341

Purple Sandpiper, 154, 160, 173, 176–178, 227, 233, 239, 316, 345, 355

Putnam, Michael S., "By the Wayside," 247–249

R

Radloff, John F., "By the Wayside," 245

Ratering, Rebecca, "By the Wayside," 353

Red-bellied Woodpecker, 9–14, 17, 86, 129, 134, 140, 163, 223, 228, 261, 263, 319, 323, 338, 341

Red-breasted Merganser, 15, 71, 88, 128, 139, 157, 226, 262, 270, 313, 343

Red-breasted Nuthatch, 9–14, 91, 129, 131, 141, 143, 164, 223, 228, 253, 264, 301, 320, 338, 341

Red Crossbill, 16, 18, 94, 130, 143, 170, 230, 265, 325

Red-eyed Vireo, 130, 133, 142, 166, 264, 300, 322, 338, 341

Red-headed Woodpecker, 9–14, 17, 80, 86, 100, 129, 131–133, 140, 163, 223, 228, 260, 263, 319, 337, 341

Red Knot, 89, 159, 263, 316, 330, 333, 358

Red-necked Grebe, 87, 110, 128, 154, 262, 311, 327, 330, 331, 342, 345, 347

Red-necked Phalarope, 154, 160, 263, 317, 335, 343

Red Phalarope, 154, 161, 173, 177

Red-shouldered Hawk, 15, 88, 128, 139, 143, 144, 158, 226, 262, 300, 302, 309, 314, 337, 340

Red-tailed Hawk, 9–14, 16, 80, 128, 139, 158, 224, 226, 261, 262, 299, 301, 314, 337, 340, 363

Red-throated Loon, 154, 262, 310

Red-winged Blackbird, 9–14, 18, 81, 130, 131, 143, 151, 169, 223, 224, 230, 265, 325, 339, 342

Redhead, 15, 80, 87, 128, 139, 156, 198, 225, 262, 270–273, 279, 282, 284, 286, 291, 293, 313, 337, 340

Ring-billed Gull, 9–14, 17, 128, 134, 140, 161, 177–180, 182, 224, 227, 239–241, 242, 243, 245, 261, 263, 317, 337, 340, 356, 357, 359–361

Ring-necked Duck, 15, 88, 128, 139, 143, 156, 198, 225, 262, 271, 272, 273, 279, 284, 285, 286, 294, 313, 337, 340

Ring-necked Pheasant, 9–14, 17, 128, 140, 151, 158, 226, 262, 314, 337, 340

Robbins, Sam, "By the Wayside," 353–354; see Hale, James and Sam Robbins

Rock Dove, 9–14, 17, 129, 131, 132, 140, 162, 227, 238, 239, 247–249, 263, 318, 337, 340

Rolley, Robert, Wisconsin Checklist Project: 1992 Update, 259–266

Rose-breasted Grosbeak, 130, 132, 142, 168, 229, 265, 300, 324, 339, 342

Rosenfield, Robert N., see Bielefeldt, John, and Robert N. Rosenfield

Ross' Goose, 310, 312, 345, 348

Rosy Finch, 252

Rough-legged Hawk, 9–14, 16, 128, 139, 158, 224, 226, 233, 238, 262, 314, 343

Royal Tern, 178

Ruby-crowned Kinglet, 15, 17, 91, 129, 141, 165, 264, 300, 302, 320, 338, 341

Ruby-throated Hummingbird, 129, 131, 132, 140, 149, 162, 263, 303, 318, 337, 341

Ruddy Duck, 15, 88, 128, 139, 157, 226, 262, 271, 272, 273, 286, 313, 337, 340

Ruddy Turnstone, 89, 140, 159, 176, 263, 316, 343, 355, 358

Rudy, Carroll, "By the Wayside," 95–96, 101, 356

Ruff, 317

Ruffed Grouse, 9–14, 17, 80, 85, 86, 128, 131, 132, 140, 158, 226, 261, 262, 314, 337, 340

Rufous-sided Towhee, 16, 18, 86, 130, 142, 168, 229, 233, 250, 265, 324, 339, 342

Rusty Blackbird, 16, 130, 143, 170, 224, 230, 265, 325, 327, 345, 365

S

Sanderling, 89, 99, 128, 133, 159, 176, 263, 316, 343, 355, 358

Sandhill Crane, 3, 15, 89, 106, 112, 128, 140, 159, 224, 227, 261, 262, 315, 337, 340

Savannah Sparrow, 16, 18, 86, 142, 144, 169, 193, 195, 229, 261, 265, 324, 339, 342

Scarlet Tanager, 86, 130, 142, 168, 265, 298, 300, 323, 339, 342

Schultz, Thomas, "By the Wayside," 239–240

Sedge Wren, 91, 141, 165, 193, 264, 320, 338, 341

Semipalmated Plover, 89, 159, 263, 315, 337, 340, 355

Semipalmated Sandpiper, 89, 160, 263, 316, 337, 340

Semo, Larry, "By the Wayside," 97, 246, 246–247

Septon, Greg, "By the Wayside," 239

Sharp-shinned Hawk, 9–14, 16, 88, 128, 133, 134, 139, 157, 224, 226, 245, 261, 262, 300, 309, 314, 337, 340

Sharp-tailed Grouse, 15, 80, 88, 158, 226, 262, 298, 300–302, 305, 314, 327–329, 343

Sharp-tailed Sparrow, 86, 94, 154, 169, 302, 324, 326, 328–330, 345, 365

Shea, Allen K., WSO Records Committee, 1–2; WSO's Response to Crow Hunting Proposal, 105–106; Christmas Bird Counts, 189; Honey Creek Work Weekend, 257; The Spring Season: 1992, 307–326

Short-billed Dowitcher, 90, 140, 160, 263, 317, 337, 340, 345, 355

Short-eared Owl, 15, 17, 90, 140, 162, 228, 263, 318, 329, 330, 343

Smith, Arthur E., Comparison of Two Wisconsin Waterfowl Census Techniques, 197–202

Snow Bunting, 9–14, 18, 143, 169, 223, 230, 265, 325

Snow Goose, 15, 128, 139, 155, 224, 262, 270, 312, 333, 348

Snowy Egret, 86, 87, 154, 155, 310, 311, 345, 347

Snowy Owl, 15, 17, 129, 162, 222, 228, 263, 318

Snowy Plover, 310, 315

Solitary Sandpiper, 89, 128, 133, 140, 159, 263, 316, 337, 340

Solitary Vireo, 92, 141, 166, 264, 300, 322, 338, 341

Song Sparrow, 9–14, 18, 81, 98, 107, 130–133, 142, 148, 169, 223, 224, 229, 248, 265, 324, 339, 342, 363

Sontag, Charles, "By the Wayside," 96, 96–97, 239, 241, 364

Sora, 85, 128, 140, 158, 262, 315, 337, 340

Soulen, Thomas K., The Summer Season: 1991, 85–94

Spahn, Robert, "By the Wayside," 100

Spotted Sandpiper, 67, 128, 140, 159, 263, 316, 337, 340

Spreeman, Michael, "By the Wayside," 245–246, 361–362

Spruce Grouse, 3, 15, 68, 80, 88, 222, 223, 226, 298–300, 304, 314

Stilt Sandpiper, 90, 140, 160, 263, 317, 329

Summer Tanager, 144, 323, 331, 363

Surf Scoter, 139, 144, 157, 225, 262, 313, 332

Swainson's Hawk, 314, 345, 354

Swainson's Thrush, 91, 129, 141, 165, 300, 321, 338, 341

Swamp Sparrow, 16, 18, 130, 143, 169, 223, 230, 265, 324, 339, 342

T

Temple, Stanley A., see Howe, Robert W., Stanley A. Temple, and Michael J. Mossman

Tennessee Warbler, 92, 130, 142, 166, 264, 322, 338, 341

Tessen, Daryl D., "By the Wayside," 98, 360, 364

Thayer's Gull, 3, 5, 15, 17, 178, 227, 233, 241, 310, 317, 345, 357, 358, 359

Townsend's Solitaire, 154, 165, 223

Tree Swallow, 86, 129, 131, 132, 134, 141, 150, 164, 264, 302, 320, 338, 341, 345, 362, 363

Trumpeter Swan, 3, 15, 79, 154, 155, 203, 204, 205, 206, 207, 209, 210, 212, 215, 216, 218, 219, 224, 312, 327–329, 343

Tufted Titmouse, 15, 17, 91, 148, 164, 228, 253, 264, 320, 327, 329, 330, 343

Tundra Swan, 15, 79, 87, 128, 139, 155, 224, 262, 270, 312, 329, 343

Turkey Vulture, 3, 15, 31–33, 35, 36, 38–41, 80, 139, 157, 262, 313, 337, 340

U

Upland Sandpiper, 85, 159, 260, 263, 302, 316, 337, 340

V

Vander Zouwen, William J., Trends in Waterfowl Use of University Bay, Lake Mendota, Wisconsin (1947–80), 267–295

Varied Thrush, 16, 141, 144, 154, 165, 223, 229

Veery, 98, 129, 141, 165, 264, 300, 301, 308, 321, 338, 341

Verch, Richard L., "By the Wayside," 183–184, 355, 361

Vesper Sparrow, 130–132, 134, 142, 144, 168, 193, 260, 265, 324, 339, 342

Vincent, Alice Clare, "By the Wayside," 249–250

Virginia Rail, 15, 17, 85, 140, 158, 262, 315, 337, 340, 354

Volkert, William K., Population Trends and Proposed Management Plans for Fourmile Island Rookery at Horicon Marsh Wildlife Area, 51–57; Survey of the Birds of the Northern Kettle Moraine Region, 137–145; Response of Grassland Birds to a Large-Scale Prairie Restoration Project, 191–196

W

Warbling Vireo, 141, 166, 264, 322, 338, 341

Water Pipit, 141, 165, 264, 321, 329, 343

Welnak, Mary Jo, "By the Wayside," 362

Western Grebe, 86, 87, 311

Western Kingbird, 129, 319

Western Meadowlark, 86, 130, 143, 170, 260, 265, 325, 339, 342

Western Sandpiper, 154, 160, 316, 329

Western Tanager, 310, 323, 335, 343

Whimbrel, 86, 89, 154, 159, 309, 316, 329, 330, 361

Whip-poor-will, 80, 86, 98, 129, 140, 162, 260, 263, 318, 337, 341, 362

White-breasted Nuthatch, 9–14, 129, 131, 132, 134, 141, 150, 164, 228, 250, 253, 261, 264, 320, 338, 341

White-crowned Sparrow, 16, 18, 130, 143, 148, 169, 223, 230, 265, 308, 310, 324, 335, 339, 342

White-eyed Vireo, 86, 92, 141, 143, 144, 321, 330, 343

White-rumped Sandpiper, 89, 160, 176, 263, 316, 328, 330–333, 343, 355

White-throated Sparrow, 9–14, 18, 94, 130, 143, 169, 223, 230, 249, 265, 324, 339, 342, 365

White-winged Crossbill, 16, 18, 94, 130, 143, 170, 223, 230, 265, 301, 325

White-winged Scoter, 157, 225, 262, 313

Whitford, Philip C., "By the Wayside," 236–237, 244–245

Wild Turkey, 9–14, 17, 80, 88, 140, 158, 226, 261, 262, 314, 337, 340

Willet, 86, 89, 140, 144, 263, 316

Willow Flycatcher, 141, 163, 261, 263, 319, 343

Wilson, Anita, see Wilson, Richard, and Anita Wilson

Wilson, Richard, and Anita Wilson, "By the Wayside," 95

Wilson's Phalarope, 90, 160, 174, 302, 317, 343

Wilson's Warbler, 86, 93, 95, 100, 142, 168, 265, 323, 339, 342

Winter Wren, 15, 17, 91, 129, 141, 143, 165, 229, 264, 299, 300, 305, 320, 338, 341

Wood, Thomas C., "By the Wayside," 348

Wood Duck, 15, 79, 128, 131, 132, 139, 150, 156, 198, 225, 261, 262, 271, 272, 302, 312, 336, 340

Wood Thrush, 86, 98, 129, 141, 144, 165, 264, 299, 300, 321, 338, 341

Worm-eating Warbler, 93, 110, 144, 323, 330, 345, 365

Y

Yellow-bellied Flycatcher, 91, 141, 163, 263, 319, 343

Yellow-bellied Sapsucker, 15, 17, 86, 129, 140, 163, 228, 300, 319, 338, 341

Yellow-billed Cuckoo, 86, 90, 129, 140, 162, 263, 318, 335

Yellow-breasted Chat, 93, 130, 134, 144, 265, 323, 330, 331

Yellow-crowned Night-Heron, 86, 87, 110, 262, 309, 312, 328, 330, 331

Yellow-headed Blackbird, 94, 143, 144, 170, 230, 265, 325, 339, 342

Yellow Rail, 88, 154, 158, 302, 309, 315, 329–331, 345, 354, 355

Yellow-rumped Warbler, 16, 92, 130, 132, 142, 167, 229, 264, 308, 322, 338, 342

Yellow-throated Vireo, 92, 130, 141, 144, 166, 261, 264, 322, 338, 341

Yellow-throated Warbler, 86, 92, 95, 98–100, 310, 322, 330, 345, 364, 365

Yellow Warbler, 81, 100, 130, 131, 142, 167, 264, 322, 338, 341

By-Laws of The Wisconsin Society for Ornithology

ARTICLE I. NAME

1.01 The name of the corporation shall be, "The Wisconsin Society for Ornithology, Inc."

1.02 The Wisconsin Society for Ornithology, Inc., is a non-stock, non-profit corporation incorporated under the laws of the State of Wisconsin.

ARTICLE II. PURPOSE

The purpose of the corporation shall be to encourage the appreciation and study of Wisconsin birds through programs in research, education, conservation, and publication.

ARTICLE III. MEMBERSHIP

3.01 *General.* Membership shall be open to all individuals interested in the objectives of the corporation as set forth in Article II.

3.02 *Application for Membership.* Application for membership shall be made in the form and manner prescribed by the Board of Directors.

3.03 *Application Approval.* Applicants for membership shall be approved upon payment of dues.

3.04 *Annual Dues.* Annual dues for regular members shall be in such amount as shall from time to time be recommended by the Board of Directors and confirmed by the membership. Dues are payable at such time and manner as the Board may specify. Any regular membership terminates if dues are 120 days in arrears.

3.05 *Life Members.* Any regular member may become a life member upon payment of a fee as determined from time to time by the Board of Directors and confirmed by the membership. Life members pay no annual dues; they may vote and are entitled to hold office.

3.06 *Honorary Members.* An honorary member is an individual who has made an outstanding contribution to the field of ornithology and is elected to honorary membership by a majority vote of the Board of Directors. A maximum of twelve individuals may be honorary members at any given time. Honorary members pay no dues; they may vote and can hold office. Honorary memberships are for the duration of the life of the person so honored.

3.07 *Removal from Membership.* Any member may be removed from membership by a majority vote of the members present at a properly called meeting of the membership, for such conduct deemed prejudicial to the corporation; provided that such member shall have first been served with written notice of the allegations against the member, and shall have been given an opportunity to produce and examine witnesses, if any, and to be heard at the meeting at which such vote is taken.

ARTICLE IV. OFFICES

4.01 *Principal and Business Offices.* The corporation may have such principal and other business offices, either within or without the State of Wisconsin, as the Board of Directors may designate or as the business of the corporation may require from time to time.

4.02 *Registered Office.* The registered office of the corporation required by the Wisconsin Nonstock Corporation Law to be maintained in the State of Wisconsin may be, but need not be, identical with the principal office in the State of Wisconsin, and the address of the registered office may be changed from time to time by the Board of Directors or by the registered agent. The business office of the registered agent of the corporation shall be identical to such registered office.

ARTICLE V. BOARD OF DIRECTORS

5.01 *General.* The Board of Directors shall be responsible for the furtherance of the purposes of the corporation, and the attainment of its objectives.

5.02 *Term and Compensation.* The Board shall be composed of a maximum of 20 persons chosen from the membership, including the five officers of the corporation. The remaining 15 Directors shall be appointed by the five officers. Members of the Board shall be appointed for a term of one year and may serve more than one term or until a successor is appointed. All Directors shall serve without compensation.

5.03 *Board Secretary.* The Secretary of the corporation shall act as the Secretary of the Board of Directors. The Secretary shall have a vote in matters considered by the board.

5.04 *General Powers.* The duties and powers of the Board shall include, but are not limited to:

(a) Managing the affairs and operations of the corporation,

(b) Adopting policies and procedures regarding membership in the corporation, and

(c) Creating committees.

5.05 *Limitations on Powers.* Notwithstanding the provisions of 5.04 above, the Board shall not have the power to:

(a) Make any decision that requires a vote by the membership at large;

(b) Commit the membership or the resources of the corporation to any project with a duration of more than two years;

(c) Merge or affiliate the corporation with any society, corporation, partnership or any other entity;

(d) Commit the financial resources of the corporation to out-of-the-ordinary expenditures. The corporation may exercise any of the powers limited by this section with the prior approval of a simple majority of the membership, voting in person at a properly called meeting of the membership.

5.06 *Quorum.* At any regular or special meeting of the members of the Board, a quorum for the transaction of business shall consist of a majority of the members of the Board.

5.07 *Removal.* Directors may be removed from office, with or without cause, by the majority vote of the Board of Directors.

5.08 *Vacancies.* Between annual meetings, vacancies on the Board shall be filled by individuals chosen by a majority vote of the officers.

ARTICLE VI. MEETINGS

6.01 *Meeting of Members.* Meetings of the membership shall take place at a time and place selected by the Board of Directors and with a minimum of 15 days written notice to the membership. Each member shall be entitled to one vote, in person, on any business coming before the meeting. The members present shall constitute a quorum to conduct business. Unless otherwise indicated by these bylaws, a simple majority of those present and voting shall be required to pass any motion at any meeting of the members.

6.02 *Meetings of the Board of Directors.*

(a) Annual Meeting. The Board of Directors shall meet at the conclusion of the Annual Membership Meeting to confirm appointment of all Board Members for the following year.

(b) Regular Meetings. The Board of Directors shall meet quarterly at a time and place to be determined by the Board. A minimum of 15 days written notice of such meetings will be made to the membership.

(c) Special Meetings. Special meetings may be held at the request of the President or a majority of the Board, at such time as the Officers may determine upon at least 15 days written notice to the Directors.

(d) Quorum. A quorum for the transaction of business at any Board of Directors meeting shall be a simple majority of the Board members. A simple majority of those present and voting shall be required to pass any motion at any meeting of the Board, unless otherwise provided herein.

6.03 *Conduct of Meetings.* The President, and in his absence a Vice President or any person chosen by the members present, shall call the meeting to order and shall act as chairman of the meeting. The Secretary of the corporation shall act as secretary of all meetings of the members, but, in the absence of the Secretary, the presiding officer may appoint any other person to act as secretary of the meeting.

6.04 *Parliamentary Authority.* The rules contained in the current edition of "*Robert's Rules of Order, Newly Revised*" or any future edition of that work shall govern the corporation's conduct in all affairs where they are applicable and not inconsistent in any way with these bylaws and/or any special rules of order the corporation may adopt.

6.05 *Proxies.* Voting by proxy will not be permitted.

6.06 *Waiver of Notice by Members.* Members of the corporation may waive any notice required to be given to them. The waiver must be in writing and shall contain the same information that would have been required to be included in the notice. It can be signed by the member at any time, before or after the time of the meeting. A proper waiver shall be deemed to be the equivalent of notice.

6.07 *Unanimous Consent Without Meeting.* Any action required or permitted by the Articles of Incorporation or by-laws or any provision of law to be taken at a meeting of the members, or directors, may be taken without a meeting if a consent in writing, setting forth the action so taken, shall be signed by all of the members entitled to vote with respect to the subject matter thereof.

ARTICLE VII. OFFICERS

7.01 *Number.* The principal officers of the corporation shall be a President, Vice-President, Secretary, Treasurer and Editor. Any two or more offices may be held by the same person, except the offices of President and Secretary and the offices of President and Vice-President.

7.02 *Election and Term of Office.* The officers are to be elected at the Annual Membership Meeting. Each officer shall hold office for a term of one year or until a successor shall have been duly elected or until death, resignation or removal.

7.03 *Removal.* Any officer or agent may be removed by the Board of Directors whenever in its judgment the best interests of the corporation will be served.

7.04 *Vacancies.* A vacancy in any principal office because of death, resignation, removal, disqualification or otherwise, shall be filled by the Board of Directors for the unexpired portion of the term.

7.05 *President.* The President shall be the principal executive officer of the corporation and, subject to the control of the Board of Directors, shall:

(a) supervise and control all of the business and affairs of the corporation;

(b) when present, preside at all meetings of the members and of the Board of Directors;

(c) have authority, subject to such rules as may be prescribed by the Board of Directors, to appoint such agents and employees of the corporation as deemed necessary, to prescribe their powers, duties and compensation, and to delegate authority to them. Such agents and employees shall hold office at the discretion of the President;

(d) have authority to sign, execute and acknowledge, on behalf of the corporation, all deeds, mortgages, bonds, stock certificates, contracts, leases, reports and all other documents or instruments necessary or proper to be executed in the course of the corporation's regular business, or which shall be authorized by resolution of the Board of Directors; and, except as otherwise provided by law or the Board of Directors, authorize any other officer or agent of the corporation to sign, execute and acknowledge such documents or instruments;

(e) in general perform all duties incident to the office of President and such other duties as may be prescribed by the Board of Directors from time to time. In the absence of the President or in the event of his death, inability or refusal to act, or in the event for any reason it shall be impracticable for the President to act personally, and in the absence of a Vice-President, the Board of Directors shall appoint one of its members to act on behalf of the President.

7.06 *Vice-President.* In the president's absence, or in the event of death or inability or refusal to act, or if for any reason it shall be impractical for the president to act personally, the vice-president shall perform the duties of the president, and when so acting, shall have all the powers of and be subject to all the restrictions upon the president. The vice-president shall perform such other duties and have such authority as from time to time may be delegated or assigned to him or her by the president or by the board of directors. These additional duties shall include, but not be limited to conducting the search process for the site of the next annual convention. The execution of any instrument of the corporation by any vice-president shall be conclusive evidence, as to third parties, of authority to act in the president's place.

7.07 *Editor.* The Editor is responsible for publication of the Society's journal "The Passenger Pigeon." The Editor is authorized by the Board of Directors, subject to their review and control, to engage a printer and commit the financial resources of the corporation for such necessary printing expenses.

7.08 *Secretary.* The Secretary shall:

(a) keep the minutes of the meetings of the members and the Board of Directors;

(b) see that all notices are duly given in accordance with the provisions of these by-laws or as required by law;

(c) be custodian of the corporate records; and

(d) in general perform all duties and exercise such authority as from time to time may be delegated or assigned to the Secretary by the President or Board of Directors.

7.09 *Treasurer.* The Treasurer shall:

(a) have charge and custody of and be responsible for all funds and securities of the corporation;

(b) receive and give receipts for monies due and payable to the corporation from any source whatsoever, and deposit all such monies in the name of the corporation in such banks, trust companies or other depositories as shall be selected in accordance with the provisions of these bylaws;

(c) keep in books or computer printouts belonging to the corporation full and accurate accounts of all receipts and disbursements,

(d) disburse the funds of the corporation in accordance with the direction of the Board of Directors or a majority of the members voting at a properly called meeting, taking proper vouchers for said disbursements and providing regular and complete reports of the financial transactions and status of the corporation at all regular meetings; and

(e) in general perform all of the duties incident to the office of Treasurer and have such other duties and exercise such other authority as from time to time may be delegated or assigned by the President or by the Board of Directors. If required by the Board of Directors, the Treasurer shall give a bond for the faithful discharge of his duties in such sum and with such surety or sureties as the Board of Directors shall determine.

7.10 *Assistant and Acting Officers.* The Board of Directors shall have the power to appoint any person to act as assistant to any officer, or as agent for the corporation in the officer's stead, or to perform the duties of such officer whenever for any reason it is impracticable for the officer to act personally. The assistant or acting officer or other agent so appointed by the Board of Directors shall have the power to perform all the duties of the office to which that person is so appointed, except as such power may be otherwise defined or restricted by the Board of Directors.

7.11 *Compensation.* The principal officers shall serve without compensation.

ARTICLE VIII. COMMITTEES

8.1 *General.* The President and/or the Board of Directors shall have the authority to establish the number and kind of special or standing committees as they determine necessary. The President shall appoint a member to chair each committee established. Chairs of standing committees shall be board members. These appointments shall be subject to the approval of the Board of Directors and shall be for a term of one year commencing at the conclusion of the Annual Meeting. The chairpersons of each committee shall submit an annual report of its activities and financial expenditures to the membership at the Annual Meeting. Committee reports shall be filed with the permanent records of the corporation.

8.2 *Standing Committees.* Standing Committees are those that are listed in each edition of the official journal of the corporation.

ARTICLE IX. NOMINATION AND ELECTION OF OFFICERS

9.01 *Nominating Committee.* In the month of January the President shall appoint a nominating committee consisting of three members of the corporation who are not current officers of the corporation. The committee shall prepare a slate of candidates for election as Officers of the Corporation to be presented to the membership at the annual meeting. The membership may also present additional nominations at the meeting.

9.02 *Election.* Officers of the corporation shall be elected by a majority of the membership present and voting at the annual meeting in person, or, in the case of no contest, by acclamation, if so moved and carried.

ARTICLE X. INDEMNITY OF OFFICERS AND DIRECTORS

10.01 *Mandatory Indemnification.* The corporation shall indemnify an officer or director to the extent that person is successful on the merits or otherwise in a proceeding, for all reasonable expenses incurred in the pro-

ceeding if the officer or director was a party because that person was an officer or director of the corporation.

10.02 *Indemnification, Exceptions.* In cases not included under Section 10.01 the corporation shall indemnify an officer or director against liability incurred by that person in a proceeding in which the officer or director is a party because of that person's status as an officer or director unless liability was incurred because that person breached or failed to perform a duty owed to the corporation and the breach or failure constitutes any of the following:

(a) A wilful failure to deal with the corporation or its members in connection with a matter in which the officer or director has a material interest.

(b) A violation of criminal law, unless the officer or director had reasonable cause to believe that the conduct was lawful or no reasonable cause to believe that the conduct was unlawful.

(c) A transaction from which the officer or director derived an improper personal profit.

(d) Wilful misconduct.

10.03 *Procedure.* Any request for indemnification must be made in writing with a detailed explanation of the circumstances giving rise to the request and the grounds for indemnification. The Board of Directors is empowered to establish a procedure for the handling of such claims.

ARTICLE XI. LIMITED LIABILITY OF OFFICERS AND DIRECTORS

Except as provided in the Wisconsin statutes, officers and directors are not liable to the corporation, its members or creditors, or any person asserting any rights on behalf of the corporation, its members or creditors, or any other person, for damages, settlements, fees, fines, penalties or other monetary liabilities arising from a breach of, or failure to perform, any duty resulting solely from the status of officer or director, unless the person asserting the liability proves that the breach or failure to perform constitutes one of the following:

(a) A wilful failure to deal fairly with the corporation or its members or creditors in connection with a matter in which the officer or director has a material conflict of interest.

(b) A violation of criminal law, unless the officer or director has reasonable cause to believe the conduct was lawful or no reasonable cause to believe the conduct was unlawful.

(c) A transaction from which the officer or director derived an improper personal profit.

(d) Wilful misconduct.

ARTICLE XII. LIMITED LIABILITY OF VOLUNTEERS

12.01 *Definition.* Volunteer means a natural person, other than an employee of the corporation, who provides services to or on behalf of the corporation without compensation.

12.02 *Immunity.* Except as provided in Section 12.03, a volunteer is not liable to any person for damages, settlements, fees, fines, penalties or other monetary liabilities arising from any act or omission as a volunteer, unless the person asserting liability proves that the act or omission constitutes any of the following:

(a) A violation of criminal law, unless the volunteer had reasonable cause to believe that the conduct was lawful, or no reasonable cause to believe that it was unlawful.

(b) Wilful misconduct.

(c) If the volunteer is an officer or director of the corporation, an act or omission within the scope of the volunteer's duties as an officer or director.

(d) Any act or omission for which the volunteer received compensation or any thing of substantial value in lieu of compensation.

12.03 *Exceptions.* This section does not apply to any of the following:

(a) A civil or criminal proceeding brought by or on behalf of any governmental unit, authority or agency.

(b) A proceeding brought by any person for a violation of state or federal law where the proceeding is brought pursuant to an express private right of action created by state or federal statute.

(c) Claims arising from the negligent operation of an automobile, truck, airplane or other vehicle by a volunteer.

(d) A proceeding against a volunteer who is licensed, certified, permitted or registered under state law and which is based upon an act or omission within the scope of practice under the volunteer's license, certificate, permit or registration.

(e) Proceedings based upon a cause of action for which the volunteer is immune from liability under any state or federal statute or regulation.

ARTICLE XIII. CORPORATE PROPERTY

All property of any kind received by the corporation shall be devoted exclusively to the furthering of the purposes of the corporation as expressed in its articles of incorporation and these bylaws.

ARTICLE XIV. TAX-EXEMPT STATUS

14.01 *General.* This corporation is non-stock and not-for-profit. It shall seek tax-exempt status from the taxing authorities and shall carry on no activity that would threaten that status.

14.02 *Net Earnings.* No part of the net earnings of the corporation shall inure to the benefit of, or be distributed to, its Board members, officers or any private persons, except that the corporation shall be authorized and empowered to pay reasonable compensation for services rendered and to make payments and distributions in furtherance of the purposes set forth in the Articles of Incorporation and these Bylaws.

14.03 *Influencing Legislation.* No substantial part of the activities of the corporation shall be the carrying on of propaganda, or otherwise attempting to influence legislation, and the corporation shall not participate in, or intervene in (including the publishing or distribution of statements) any political campaign on behalf of or against any candidate for public office.

14.04 *Prohibited Activities.* Notwithstanding any other provision of these by-laws, the corporation shall not carry on any other activities not permitted to be carried on by a corporation exempt from the Federal Income Tax under Section 501(c)(3) of the Internal Revenue Code.

ARTICLE XV. ENDOWMENT FUNDS

The corporation may establish Endowment Funds into which all monies received from Life Memberships, and any other membership categories the Board may specify, together with any gifts, bequests or devises, specifically directed thereto. These funds shall be segregated from all other accounts and be administered by the Treasurer.

ARTICLE XVI. AMENDMENT

These by-laws may be amended by two-thirds vote of the Board members then in office, after fifteen days written notice of the proposed changes and the date on which such vote will be taken. No amendment shall be inconsistent with any provision of the Articles of Incorporation or any provision of law.

ARTICLE XVII. MISCELLANEOUS

17.01 *Fiscal Year.* The fiscal year of the corporation shall be the calendar year.

17.02 *Dissolution.* In the event of any dissolution of the corporation, full or partial, in any manner or for any reason, the assets of the corporation which remain after making provision for the outstanding obligations of the corporation, shall be distributed exclusively to organizations organized and operated solely for purposes in keeping with the requirements of Section 501(c)(3) of the Internal Revenue Code of 1954 as subsequently amended, as the Board with the approval of the members, shall determine, and in accordance with the lawful activities and purposes of the corporation.

17.03 *Adoption of By-laws.* These by-laws shall be adopted by a majority vote of the Board of Directors voting at a properly noticed Board Meeting at the time of their proposal for adoption. The by-laws shall be in full force and effect immediately upon their adoption.

17.04 *Seal.* This corporation shall have no seal.

17.05 *Policy and Procedure Manual.* The Board of Directors may establish a procedure manual to further define the corporation policy and procedures. This manual shall not be inconsistent with the Articles of Incorporation, these By-laws or any provision of law. After approval this Procedure Manual may be modified by the Board of Directors with a simple majority vote.

Adopted on the 18th day of July, 1992, as a restatement of the Bylaws of the corporation intended to supersede any and all prior bylaws and their amendments, by the Board of Directors of The Wisconsin Society for Ornithology, Inc.

NOTICES AND ADVERTISEMENTS

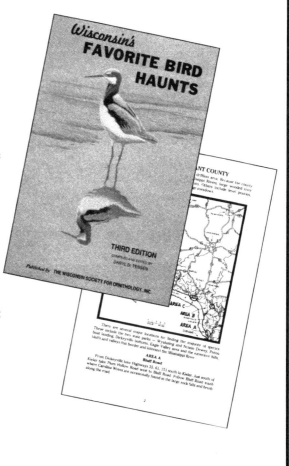